Hymnal

Worldwide Church of God

ISBN 1-55825-335-1

Published by
Worldwide Church of God
Pasadena, California
August, 1993

Printed by
R. R. Donnelley & Sons Company
Crawfordsville, Indiana, U.S.A.

"To the chosen lady and
her children..."

(2 John 1 NIV)

Preface

*"Let the word of Christ dwell in you richly as you teach
and admonish one another with all wisdom, and as you
sing psalms, hymns and spiritual songs with
gratitude in your hearts to God."*

(Colossians 3:16 NIV)

Singing hymns has always been an integral part of
Christian worship. But have you ever wondered why we sing?

Singing psalms, hymns and spiritual songs helps us develop
a closer relationship with our Creator by directing our thoughts
toward God and His eternal purpose for the human family.

Singing helps unify the congregation in an inspirational
endeavor which draws us closer together as God's united
spiritual family.

Singing enables us to express our devotion to God in
praise, to participate in worship services as individuals, and to be
actively involved in expressing our appreciation to God.

Singing songs based on the wonderful truths revealed in
the Word of God helps us celebrate and rejoice in the good
news of the message of the Gospel.

Singing songs of praise helps us to deepen our appreciation
of the importance of Christ's sacrifice and His daily presence in
our lives through the Holy Spirit.

As part of God's great worldwide family, let us
enthusiastically *"serve the Lord with gladness,"* lifting our voices in
united praise. Let us humbly and gratefully *"come before His
presence with singing."*

The Publisher

Acknowledgments

The music contained in this hymnal has been produced as a service to the Worldwide Church of God by the Music Department of Ambassador College.

—— EDITORIAL BOARD ——
Joseph W. Tkach, Editor in Chief
J. Michael Feazell, Assistant to the Editor in Chief
Joseph W. Tkach Jr., Director, Church Administration
Greg R. Albrecht, L. Leroy Neff, Larry R. Salyer, Donald L. Ward, Advisers
Ross F. Jutsum, General Editor

—— HYMNAL DESIGN ——
Michael F. Riley

—— MUSIC DESIGN AND LAYOUT ——
Thomas Crabb, (Special Consultant)
Sarah Bilowus, Bruce Hedges
Rick Peterson

—— MUSIC SELECTION AND ARRANGEMENT ——
Gerald Bieritz, David Bilowus, Sarah Bilowus
Roger Bryant, Thomas Crabb, Paul Heisler, Ross Jutsum, Ruth Myrick

—— PROOFREADING ——
David Bilowus, Sarah Bilowus, Thomas Crabb
Paula Marler Johnson, Suzanne Mauzey, Ruth Myrick

—— PRODUCTION ASSISTANTS ——
Elizabeth Adlington, Philip C. Dick, Irene Hart, Joanne Hutchison
Julia Meek, Ja'nean Klar Mentell, John Myers, Rick Peterson
Linda Hirschler Ross, Kathryn Bullock Sherrod
Michael Snellgrove, Cynthia Kendall Taylor

—— PHOTOGRAPHY ——
H. Armstrong Roberts

The Worldwide Church of God and the Music Department of Ambassador College wish to sincerely thank the Editorial, Legal and Publishing departments, as well as the many other individuals who contributed to this Hymnal.

Table Of Contents

Christ, Our Lord, Savior and King
Christian Living
Creation
Faithfulness, Guidance and Protection
God's Blessings and Our Thanksgiving
God's Greatness and Power
God's Love, Mercy and Patience
God's Plan of Salvation
Praise, Worship and Adoration
Prayer and Supplication
The Church of God
The Family of God
The Word of God

All Things Bright and Beautiful

"And God saw every thing that He had made, and, behold, it was very good" (Genesis 1:31)

With thanksgiving

All things bright and beau - ti - ful, all crea - tures great and small,

All things wise and won - der - ful, the Lord God made them all.

1. Each lit - tle flow'r that o - pens, each lit - tle bird that sings,
2. The pur - ple - head - ed moun - tain, the riv - er run - ning by,
3. The cold wind in the win - ter, the pleas - ant sum - mer sun,
4. He gave us eyes to see them, and lips that we might tell

He made their glow - ing col - ors, He made their ti - ny wings:
The sun - set, and the morn - ing that bright - ens up the sky:
The ripe fruits in the gar - den, He made them ev - 'ry one:
How great is God Al - might - y Who has made all things well:

TEXT: Cecil Frances Alexander
MUSIC: William Henry Monk

O Perfect Love

"A man... shall cleave unto his wife: and they shall be one flesh" (Genesis 2:24)

Devotedly

1. O per-fect Love, all hu-man thought tran-scend - ing,
2. O per-fect Life, be Thou their full as - sur - ance
3. Grant them the joy which bright-ens earth-ly sor - row;

Low - ly we kneel in prayer be - fore Thy throne,
Of ten - der char - i - ty and stead-fast faith,
Grant them the peace which calms all earth - ly strife,

That theirs may be the love which knows no end - ing,
Of pa - tient hope, and qui - et, brave en - dur - ance,
And to life's day the glo - rious un-known mor - row

Whom Thou for - ev - er-more dost join in one.
With child - like trust that fears not pain or death.
That dawns up - on e - ter-nal love and life.

TEXT: Dorothy Gurney
MUSIC: Joseph Barnby

I Will Sing Unto the Eternal

"I will sing unto the Lord, for He hath triumphed gloriously" (Exodus 15:1)

Triumphantly

1. I will sing un-to the E-ter-nal; He has tri-umphed glo-rious-ly!
2. "I will chase them and o-ver-take them, catch them and di-vide the spoil;"
3. Peo-ple heard and na-tions trem-bled; dread and ter-ror on them fell;

He has stretched out His right hand and hurled the foe in-to the sea!
Said the foe, "My hand will de-stroy them," but the foe drowned in the sea!
Chiefs of E-dom all were a-mazed, and they all trem-bled in their fear!

O E-ter-nal, You are my strength, my song, my great sal-va - tion!
O E-ter-nal, at Your blast the wa-ters gath-ered, depths con-gealed!
Pha-raoh's horse-men and his char-iots sank in-to the churn-ing sea!

O E-ter-nal, You are my God and I will glo-ri-fy Your name!
O E-ter-nal, who can be like You, glo-ri-ous in ho-li-ness?
O E-ter-nal, You led Your peo-ple o-ver dry land through the sea!

TEXT: Exodus 15:1-19
MUSIC: Dwight Armstrong

Remember the Sabbath Day

"...to keep it holy" (Exodus 20:8)

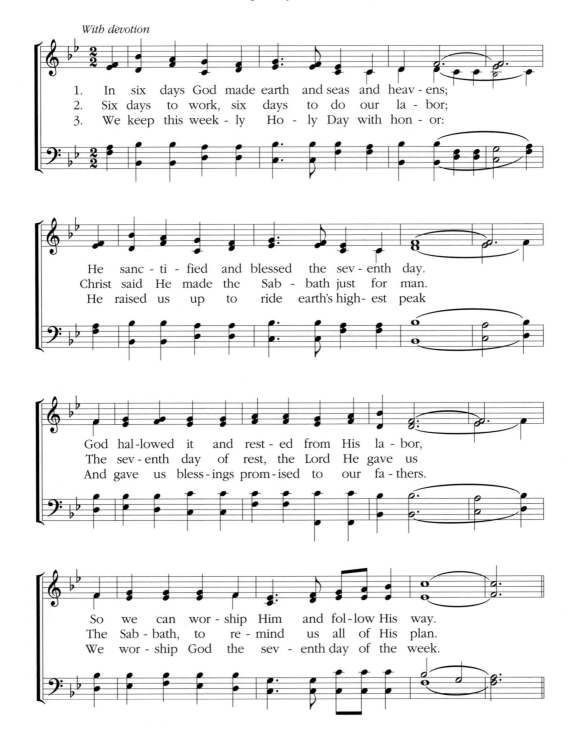

With devotion

1. In six days God made earth and seas and heav-ens;
2. Six days to work, six days to do our la-bor;
3. We keep this week-ly Ho-ly Day with hon-or:

He sanc-ti-fied and blessed the sev-enth day.
Christ said He made the Sab-bath just for man.
He raised us up to ride earth's high-est peak

God hal-lowed it and rest-ed from His la-bor,
The sev-enth day of rest, the Lord He gave us
And gave us bless-ings prom-ised to our fa-thers.

So we can wor-ship Him and fol-low His way.
The Sab-bath, to re-mind us all of His plan.
We wor-ship God the sev-enth day of the week.

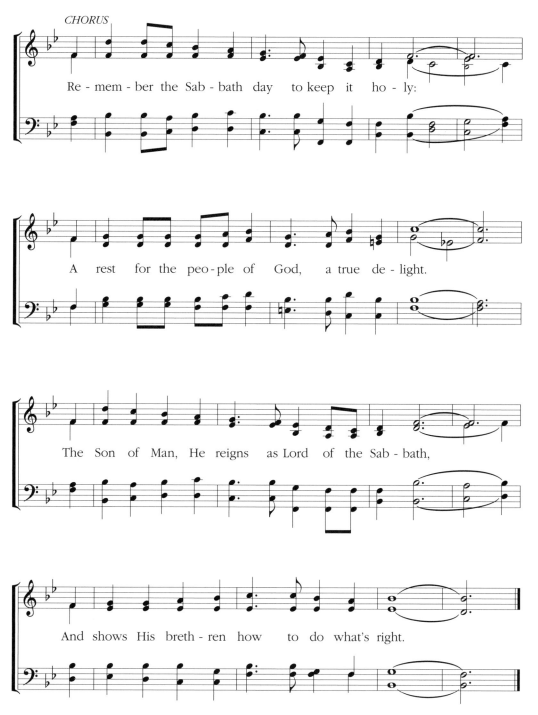

CHORUS

Re - mem - ber the Sab - bath day to keep it ho - ly:

A rest for the peo - ple of God, a true de - light.

The Son of Man, He reigns as Lord of the Sab - bath,

And shows His breth - ren how to do what's right.

TEXT: Exodus 20:8-10, Isaiah 58:13-14 & Mark 2:27-28
MUSIC: Ross Jutsum

Honor Your Father and Mother

"...that thy days may be long upon the land" (Exodus 20:12)

With wholehearted devotion

1. Hon - or your fa - ther and moth - er,
2. Christ, son of Jo - seph and Mar - y,
3. Heav'n - ly Je - ru - s'lem for - ev - er,

That your days may be long on the land.
Whose fa - ther and moth - er we know,
It is free and the moth - er of all.

Boun - ti - ful bless - ings for - ev - er,
Left us a per - fect ex - am - ple
How much our heav - en - ly Fa - ther

The E - ter - nal your God did com - mand.
To fol - low wher - ev - er we go.
Gives gifts to the chil - dren He calls.

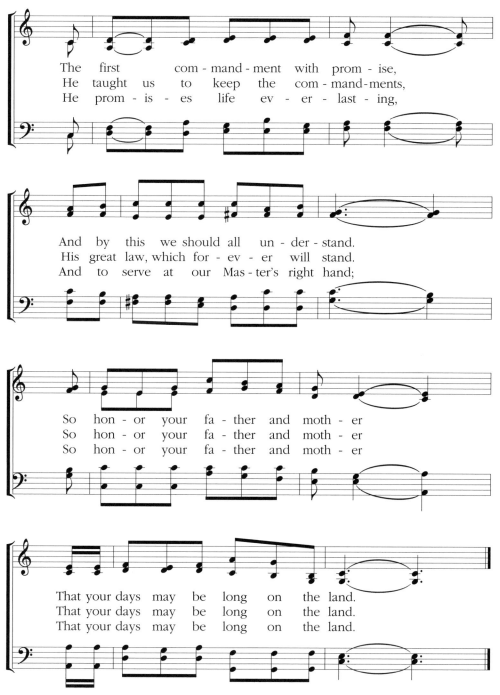

The first com - mand - ment with prom - ise,
He taught us to keep the com - mand - ments,
He prom - is - es life ev - er - last - ing,

And by this we should all un - der - stand.
His great law, which for - ev - er will stand.
And to serve at our Mas - ter's right hand;

So hon - or your fa - ther and moth - er
So hon - or your fa - ther and moth - er
So hon - or your fa - ther and moth - er

That your days may be long on the land.
That your days may be long on the land.
That your days may be long on the land.

TEXT: Exodus 20:12, Matthew 25:23, Luke 2:51-52, & James 1:17
MUSIC: Ross Jutsum

8

Who Is on the Lord's Side?

"Who is on the Lord's side?" (Exodus 32:26)

With conviction

1. Who is on the Lord's side? Who will serve the King?
2. Not for weight of glo - ry, nor for crown and palm,
3. Je - sus, Thou hast bought us, not with gold or gem,
4. Fierce may be the con - flict, strong may be the foe,

Who will be His help - ers, oth - er lives to bring?
En - ter we the ar - my, raise the war - rior-psalm;
But with Thine own life - blood, for Thy di - a - dem;
But the King's own ar - my none can o - ver-throw;

Who will leave the world's side? Who will face the foe?
But for love that claim - eth lives for whom He died:
With Thy bless - ing fill - ing each who comes to Thee,
'Round His stan - dard rang - ing, vic - tory is se - cure,

Who is on the Lord's side? Who for Him will go?
He whom Je - sus nam - eth must be on His side.
Thou hast made us will - ing; Thou hast made us free.
For His truth un - chang-ing makes the tri - umph sure.

By Thy call of mer - cy, by Thy grace di - vine,
By Thy love con-strain - ing, by Thy grace di - vine,
By Thy grand re - demp - tion, by Thy grace di - vine,
Joy - ful - ly en - list - ing, by Thy grace di - vine,

We are on the Lord's side; Sav - ior, we are Thine!
We are on the Lord's side; Sav - ior, we are Thine!
We are on the Lord's side; Sav - ior, we are Thine!
We are on the Lord's side; Sav - ior, we are Thine!

TEXT: Frances R. Havergal
MUSIC: C. Luise Reichardt

Come, Thou Almighty King

"I pray Thee, go among us...and take us for Thine inheritance" (Exodus 34:9)

Majestically

1. Come, Thou Al - might - y King,
2. Come, Thou In - car - nate Word,
3. Come, Ho - ly Ad - vo - cate,

Help us Thy name to sing; help us to praise:
Gird on Thy might - y sword; and us de - fend.
A pure heart in us cre - ate, in this glad hour.

Fa - ther, all glo - ri - ous, o'er all vic - to - ri - ous,
Come, and Thy peo - ple bless, and give Thy word suc - cess;
Thou, who al - might - y art, o - pen our minds to see

Come and reign o - ver us, An - cient of Days.
Spir - it of ho - li - ness, our prayer at - tend.
What Christ would have us be, Spir - it of pow'r.

TEXT: Author Unknown
MUSIC: Felice de Giardini

Proclaim Holy Convocations

"These are the feasts of the Lord…which ye shall proclaim in their seasons" (Leviticus 23:4)

With joy and earnestness

1. Our God spoke to Mo-ses, say-ing, De-clare un-to Is-ra-el
2. Six days shall your work be fin-ished; the sev-enth, the Sab-bath rest.
3. God gave us the ho-ly feast days to pic-ture His mas-ter plan;

The feasts of the Lord, por-tray-ing my plan for man-kind I fore-tell.
No work shall be un-der-tak-en till sun-set has come in the west.
To show us His love for-ev-er, His love for the fam-'ly of man.

CHORUS

Pro-claim ho-ly con-vo-ca-tions, the times and the sea-sons I give;

And teach them my rev-e-la-tions, so you and your seed might live.

TEXT: Leviticus 23 & Deuteronomy 30
MUSIC: Ross Jutsum

The Lord Bless You and Keep You

"The Lord bless thee, and keep thee... and make His face to shine upon thee" (Numbers 6:24, 25)

Prayerfully

The Lord bless you and keep you;

The Lord lift His coun - te - nance up - on you,

and give you peace, and give you peace;

and give you peace, and give you peace;

The Lord make His face to shine up - on you,

The Lord make His face to shine up - on you,

And be gra - cious un - to you, be gra - cious,
And be gra - cious and be gra - cious,

The Lord be gra - cious, gra - cious un - to you.

TEXT: Numbers 6:24-26
MUSIC: BENEDICTION by Peter C. Lutkin

Be Thou My Vision

"Leave us not, I pray thee...and thou mayest be to us instead of eyes" (Numbers 10:31)

Meditatively

1. Be Thou my Vi - sion, O Lord of my heart;
2. Be Thou my Wis - dom, and Thou my true Word;
3. Rich - es I heed not, nor man's emp - ty praise,

Nought be all else to me, save that Thou art.
I ev - er with Thee and Thou with me, Lord;
Thou mine in - her - i - tance, now and al - ways:

Thou my best thought, by day or by night,
Thou my great Fa - ther, I Thy true son;
Thou and Thou on - ly first in my heart,

Wak - ing or sleep - ing, Thy pres - ence my light.
Thou in me dwell - ing, and I with Thee one.
High King of heav - en, my Trea - sure Thou art.

TEXT: Ancient Irish, transcribed by Mary Byrne; versified by Eleanor Hull
MUSIC: SLANE, traditional Irish melody; harmonization by David Evans

America the Beautiful

"For the Lord thy God bringeth thee into a good land…" (Deuteronomy 8:7)

With dignity and appreciation

1. O beau - ti - ful for spa - cious skies, for am - ber waves of grain;
2. O beau - ti - ful for pil - grim feet, whose stern, im - pas - sioned stress,
3. O beau - ti - ful for he - roes proved in lib - er - at - ing strife,
4. O beau - ti - ful for pa - triot dream that sees be - yond the years;

For pur - ple moun - tain maj - es - ties, a - bove the fruit - ed plain!
A thor - ough - fare for free - dom beat, a - cross the wil - der - ness!
Who more than self their coun - try loved, and mer - cy more than life!
Thine al - a - bas - ter cit - ies gleam, un - dimmed by hu - man tears!

A - mer - i - ca! A - mer - i - ca! God shed His grace on thee,
A - mer - i - ca! A - mer - i - ca! God mend thine ev - 'ry flaw,
A - mer - i - ca! A - mer - i - ca! May God thy gold re - fine,
A - mer - i - ca! A - mer - i - ca! God shed His grace on thee,

And crown thy good with broth - er - hood, from sea to shin - ing sea!
Con - firm thy soul in self - con - trol, thy lib - er - ty in law!
Till all suc - cess be no - ble - ness and ev - 'ry grace di - vine!
And crown thy good with broth - er - hood, from sea to shin - ing sea!

TEXT: Katherine Lee Bates
MUSIC: Samuel Ward

Give of Your Best to the Master

"for consider how great things He hath done for you" (1 Samuel 12:24)

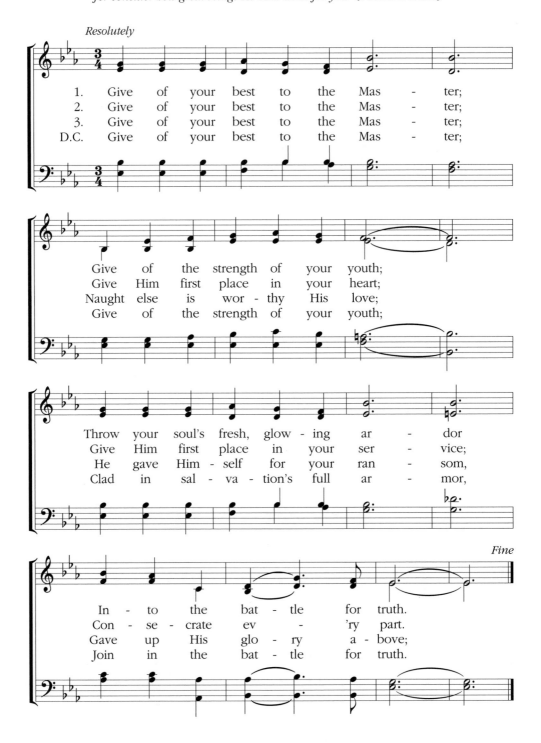

Resolutely

1. Give of your best to the Mas - ter;
2. Give of your best to the Mas - ter;
3. Give of your best to the Mas - ter;
D.C. Give of your best to the Mas - ter;

Give of the strength of your youth;
Give Him first place in your heart;
Naught else is wor - thy His love;
Give of the strength of your youth;

Throw your soul's fresh, glow - ing ar - dor
Give Him first place in your ser - vice;
He gave Him - self for your ran - som,
Clad in sal - va - tion's full ar - mor,

Fine

In - to the bat - tle for truth.
Con - se - crate ev - 'ry part.
Gave up His glo - ry a - bove;
Join in the bat - tle for truth.

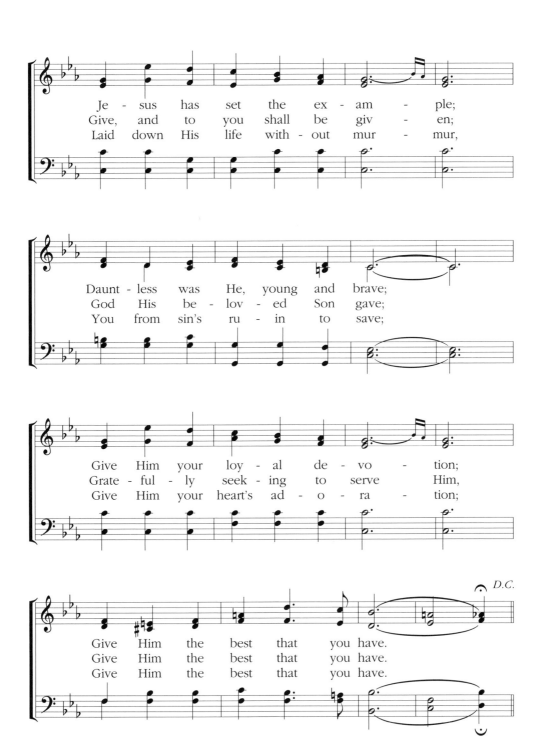

Je - sus has set the ex - am - ple;
Give, and to you shall be giv - en;
Laid down His life with - out mur - mur,

Daunt - less was He, young and brave;
God His be - lov - ed Son gave;
You from sin's ru - in to save;

Give Him your loy - al de - vo - tion;
Grate - ful - ly seek - ing to serve Him,
Give Him your heart's ad - o - ra - tion;

D.C.

Give Him the best that you have.
Give Him the best that you have.
Give Him the best that you have.

TEXT: Howard B. Grose
MUSIC: Mrs. Charles Barnard

18

Trust and Obey

"To obey is better than sacrifice" (I Samuel 15:22)

With devotion

1. When we walk with the Lord in the light of His Word,
2. Not a shad - ow can rise, not a cloud in the skies,
3. Not a bur - den we bear, not a sor - row we share,
4. Then in fel - low - ship sweet we will sit at His feet,

What a glo - ry He sheds on our way!
But His smile quick - ly drives it a - way;
But our toil He doth rich - ly re - pay;
Or we'll walk by His side in the way;

While we do His good will, He a - bides with us still,
Not a doubt or a fear, not a sigh or a tear,
Not a grief or a loss, not a frown or a cross,
What He says we will do; where He sends we will go;

And with all who will trust and o - bey.
Can re - main when we trust and o - bey.
But is blest if we trust and o - bey.
Nev - er fear, on - ly trust and o - bey.

Trust and o - bey, for there's no oth - er way

To be hap - py in Je - sus, but to trust and o - bey.

TEXT: James H. Sammis
MUSIC: Daniel B. Towner

Let All Things Now Living

"Sing unto the Lord, all the earth; show forth from day to day His salvation" (I Chronicles 16:23)

With joyful praise

1. Let all things now liv - ing a song of thanks - giv - ing
2. His law He en - forc - es: the stars in their cours - es,

To God the Cre - a - tor tri - um - phant - ly raise,
The sun in His or - bit, o - be - dient - ly shine;

Who fash - ioned and made us, pro - tect - ed and stayed us,
The hills and the moun - tains, the riv - ers and foun - tains,

Who guid - eth us on to the end of our days.
The deeps of the o - cean pro - claim Him di - vine.

His ban - ners are o'er us, His light goes be - fore us,
We, too, should be voic - ing our love and re - joic - ing;

A pil - lar of fire shin - ing forth in the night,
With glad ad - o - ra - tion a song let us raise,

'Til shad - ows have van - ished and dark - ness is ban - ished,
'Til all things now liv - ing u - nite in thanks - giv - ing

As for - ward we trav - el from light in - to light.
To God in the high - est, ho - san - na and praise!

TEXT: *Katherine K. Davis*
MUSIC: *Traditional Welsh melody, ASH GROVE*

Now Thank We All Our God

"Now therefore, our God, we thank Thee, and praise Thy glorious name" (I Chronicles 29:13)

Gratefully

1. Now thank we all our God with hearts and hands and voic - es,
2. O may this boun-teous God through all our lives be near us,
3. All praise and thanks to God, the Fa - ther, now be giv - en,

Who won-drous things hath done, in Whom His Church re - joic - es,
With ev - er joy - ful hearts and bless - ed peace to cheer us,
The Son, the one who reigns with Him in high - est heav - en,

Who from our moth - ers' arms hath blessed us on our way
And keep us in His grace, and guide us when per - plexed,
The one E - ter - nal God, Whom earth and heav'n a - dore;

With count - less gifts of love, and still is ours to - day.
And free us from all ills in this world and the next.
For thus it was, is now, and shall be ev - er - more.

TEXT: Martin Rinkart, 1636; translated by Catherine Winkworth, 1858
MUSIC: Johann Cruger, 1647; from Mendelssohn's "Hymn of Praise," 1840

Blest and Happy Is the Man

"Blessed is the man that walketh not in the counsel of the ungodly" (Psalm 1:1)

Joyfully

1. Blest and hap - py is the man who does nev - er walk a - stray,
2. Ne'er in scorn - ers' chair he sits, for he plac - es his de - light
3. He shall be a tree that grows, plant - ed by the riv - er's side,

Nor with the un - god - ly men stands in sin - ners' way.
In God's law and med - i - tates on it day and night.
Which in sea - son yields its fruit; green its leaves a - bide.

CHORUS

All he does pros - pers well, but the wick - ed are not so;

They are chaff be - fore the wind, driv - en to and fro.

TEXT: Psalm 1
MUSIC: Dwight Armstrong

Trust in God and Stand in Awe

"Hear me when I call, O God of my righteousness" (Psalm 4:1)

Reverently, with confidence

1. Hear and an-swer when I call, O righ-teous God.
2. O how long will sons of men love van-i-ty?
3. "O that we might see some good!" man-y will say;

From dis-tress You set me free; hear now my prayer.
O how long love vain in-trigues, seek af-ter lies?
On-ly look and smile on us, O righ-teous God!

O how men love van-i-ty; false-hood they seek;
Trust in God and stand in awe, and cease to sin.
God has giv-en me more joy than they all know;

Turn-ing glo-ry in-to shame, they are mis-led.
Know that God has set a-part all god-ly men.
He a-lone makes me to dwell safe-ly in peace.

TEXT: Psalm 4
MUSIC: Dwight Armstrong

Give Ear Unto My Words, O Lord

"Hearken unto the voice of my cry, my King, and my God" (Psalm 5:2)

Prayerfully

1. Give ear un - to my words, O Lord, my med - i - ta - tion weigh;
2. For Thou art not a God who does in wick - ed - ness de - light;
3. But I in - to Thy house will come in Thy a - bun - dant grace;
4. Let all who trust in Thee be glad, in shouts their praise pro - claim;

Hear my loud cry, my King, my God, for I to Thee will pray.
No e - vil shall a - bide with Thee, nor fools stand in Thy sight.
And I will wor - ship in Thy fear to - ward Thy ho - ly place.
Thou sav - est them; let all re - joice who love Thy ho - ly name.

Lord, Thou shalt ear - ly hear my voice; I ear - ly will di - rect
All e - vil - do - ers Thou dost hate, cut off shall li - ars be;
Be - cause of watch - ful en - e - mies, O lead me by Thy grace,
For Lord, un - to the righ - teous man Thou wilt Thy bless - ing yield;

My prayer to Thee, and look - ing up, an an - swer will ex - pect.
The blood - y and de - ceit - ful man ab - hor - red is by Thee.
And in Thy righ - teous - ness, Thy way make straight be - fore my face.
With fa - vor Thou wilt com - pass him a - bout as with a shield.

TEXT: Psalm 5
MUSIC: Dwight Armstrong

Turn, O God, and Save Me

"In the grave who shall give Thee thanks?" (Psalm 6:5)

Broadly and earnestly

1. O Lord God, re - buke me not in an - ger,
2. O Lord God, how long are You in help - ing?
3. O Lord God, my bed is wet with weep - ing,

Nor in hot dis - plea - sure chas - tise me, O God.
Turn, O God, and save me; de - liv - er my soul,
And I faint with moan - ing be - cause of my foes.

Be gra - cious, Lord, and show me Your mer - cy;
For Your great love, for the sake of Your mer - cies;
But God has heard; He has an - swered my prayer.

Heal me, O God, for I lan - guish and ache.
For in the grave there is no thought of You.
My foes shall turn, and shall be a - shamed.

TEXT: Psalm 6
MUSIC: Dwight Armstrong

How Excellent Is Thy Name!

"O Lord our Lord, how excellent is Thy name in all the earth!" (Psalm 8:1)

With exultation; in stately rhythm

1. How ex - cel - lent in all the earth, Lord our Lord is Thy name!
2. When I look up un - to the heav'ns which Thine own fin - gers framed,
3. For Thou hast made him lit - tle less than the an - gels a - bove,

Who hast Thy glo - ry far ad - vanced a - bove the star - ry frame.
Un - to the moon and to the stars, which were by Thee or - dained;
With glo - ry and with dig - ni - ty, with hon - or crowned his head.

From mouths of babes and in - fants, Lord, strength by Thee is or - dained,
Then say I, what is man that Thou should be mind - ful of him?
Ap - point - ed lord of all Thy works, all things un - der his feet:

So that Thine en - e - mies be stilled, Thy venge - ful foes re - strained.
Or what, the son of man, that Thou so kind to him should be?
All sheep and ox - en, yea, and beasts that in the field do stray.

TEXT: Psalm 8:1-7
MUSIC: Dwight Armstrong

I Will Praise Thee, O Eternal!

"I will show forth all Thy marvelous works" (Psalm 9:1)

Triumphantly

1. I will praise Thee, O E - ter - nal; I will show forth Thy great works!
2. The E - ter - nal lives for - ev - er; He de - stroys all wick - ed men;
3. To the Lord who dwells in Zi - on, sing to Him and praise His name!

O Thou Most High God, E - ter - nal, I will sing praise to Thy name!
He re - moves their name for - ev - er, and their mem - 'ry dies with them.
Tell His deeds a - mong the na - tions! Tell of all His glo - rious works!

But my foes shall turn and stum - ble; at Thy pres - ence they shall fall.
But He judg - es all with fair - ness; He will rule with eq - ui - ty;
He a - veng - es all His peo - ple; He will not for - get their cry.

The E - ter - nal judg - es right - ly, and for - ev - er He will rule!
All who know His name shall trust Him; He will not for - sake His own.
To the Lord who dwells in Zi - on, sing to Him and praise His name!

TEXT: Psalm 9:1-12
MUSIC: Dwight Armstrong

Declare His Works to All Nations!

"Sing praises to the Lord, which dwelleth in Zion: declare among the people His doings" (Psalm 9:11)

With great exultation

1. I will sing, O Most High, prais-es to Thy name with my whole heart!
2. God will rule up-right-ly, judge the world in righ-teous-ness.
3. God Most High in Zi-on dwells; He will not for-get His peo - ple;

And pro-claim Thy won-ders great; I will re-joice and ex-ult in Thee!
The op-pressed who seek Him, He will to them a ref-uge be.
They de-clare His great works, and He will not for - get their cry.

My foes fall at Thy sight, for Thou hast main-tained my cause and my cry;
For the Lord will not for-get those who put their trust and con-fi-dence in Him.
Rise, O Lord! Put them all in fear! All the na-tions that for-get that Thou art God.

God will judge from His throne; He shall re-main for - ev - er-more!
To the Lord sing His praise; de-clare His works to all na - tions!
Judge them, Lord, in Thy sight; let the na-tions know they are but men!

TEXT: Psalm 9:1-4, 7-12, 19, 20
MUSIC: Dwight Armstrong

The Lord Is King

"...for ever and ever" (Psalm 10:16)

Majestically

1. The Lord is King! Lift up your voice,
2. The Lord is King! Who then shall dare
3. The Lord is King! Child of the dust.
4. One Lord, one em - pire, all se - cures;

O earth and all ye heav-ens, re - joice.
Re - sist His will, dis - trust His care,
The Judge of all the earth is just;
He reigns and life and death are Yours.

From world to world the joy shall ring,
Or mur - mur at His wise de - crees,
Ho - ly and true are all His ways;
Through earth and heav'n one song shall ring,

"The Lord om - nip - o - tent is King!"
Or doubt His roy - al prom - is - es?
Let ev - 'ry crea - ture speak His praise.
"The Lord om - nip - o - tent is King!"

TEXT: Josiah Condert, 1824, based on Psalm 10:16-18
MUSIC: Arrangement from Franz Joseph Haydn's "Creation," 1798

Who Shall Dwell on Thy Holy Hill?

"He that walketh uprightly, and worketh righteousness, and speaketh the truth in his heart" (Psalm 15:2)

Meditatively

1. O E - ter - nal, who shall dwell in the tem - ple of Thy grace?
2. He who ne'er with slan - der-ing tongue ut-ters mal - ice and de - ceit;

Who shall on Thy ho - ly hill have a fixed a - bid - ing place?
Who will ne'er his neigh - bor wrong, nor a slan - d'rous tale re - peat.

He who walks in righ-teous-ness, all his ac - tions just and clear;
Who will claim no u - su - ry, nor with bribes pol - lute his hand;

He whose words the truth ex - press, spo - ken from a heart sin - cere.
He who thus shall frame his life, shall un-moved for - ev - er stand.

TEXT: Psalm 15
MUSIC: Dwight Armstrong

Forth in Thy Name

"I have set the Lord always before me" (Psalm 16:8)

Resolutely

1. Forth in Thy name, O Lord, I go,
2. The task Thy wis - dom hath as - signed,
3. Thee may I set at my right hand,

My dai - ly la - bor to pur - sue.
O let me cheer - ful - ly ful - fill:
Whose eyes my in - most sub - stance see.

Thee, on - ly Thee, re - solved to know,
In all my works Thy pres - ence find,
And la - bor on at Thy com - mand,

In all I think, or speak, or do.
And prove Thy good and per - fect will.
And of - fer all my works to Thee.

TEXT: Charles Wesley, 1749
MUSIC: "Easy Church Music For Choirs," 1853, based on Psalm 16:8

Thee Will I Love, O Lord

"I will love Thee, O Lord, my strength" (Psalm 18:1)

With confidence and joy

1. Thee will I love, O Lord, my might, my rock, my help, my sav-ing pow'r,
2. In my dis-tress I called on God, to the E-ter-nal raised my prayer;
3. His dead-ly shafts a-round He threw; His foes dis-persed in wild re-treat;
4. For who but God should be a-dored? Who but our God can us be-friend?

My God, my trust, my shield in fight, my great sal-va-tion, my high tow'r!
My voice He from His tem-ple heard; my cry as-cend-ed to His ear.
Like burn-ing darts His light-nings flew, scat-ter-ing them in sore de-feat.
Who is a rock be-sides the Lord? Who else is a-ble to de-fend?

To the E-ter-nal is my prayer, to whom all praise we owe;
He bowed the heav'ns His high a-bode, came in the dark of night;
He sent from heav'n and res-cued me from wa-ters swell-ing high;
On the E-ter-nal I re-lied, and o-ver foes pre-vailed;

So shall I by His watch-ful care safe-ly be guard-ed from my foe.
He on a cher-ub swift-ly rode, and on the wings of wind His flight.
From those that hate me set me free, and foes that stron-ger were than I.
With the Al-might-y on my side, their lof-ty walls I fear-less scaled.

TEXT: Psalm 18 & II Samuel 22
MUSIC: Dwight Armstrong

A Mighty Fortress Is Our God

"The Lord is my rock, and my fortress, and my deliverer" (Psalm 18:2)

Steadfastly

1. A might-y for-tress is our God, a bul-wark nev-er fail - ing;
2. Did we in our own strength con-fide, our striv-ing would be los - ing,
3. That word a-bove all earth-ly pow'rs, no thanks to them, a-bid - eth;

Our help-er He, a-mid the flood of mor-tal ills pre-vail - ing:
Were not the right Man on our side, the Man of God's own choos - ing:
The Spir-it and the gifts are ours through Him who with us sid - eth;

For still our an-cient foe doth seek to work us woe;
Dost ask who that may be? Christ Je-sus, it is He;
Let goods and kin-dred go, this mor-tal life al - so;

His craft and pow'r are great, and armed with cru-el hate;
Lord Sab-a-oth, His name, from age to age the same,
The bod-y they may kill: God's truth a-bid-eth still;

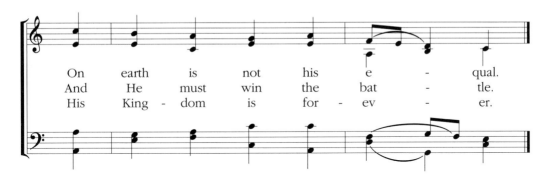

On earth is not his e - qual.
And He must win the bat - tle.
His King - dom is for - ev - er.

TEXT: Martin Luther; translated by Frederick H. Hedge
MUSIC: Martin Luther

The Heavens God's Glory Do Declare

"...and the firmament showeth His handywork" (Psalm 19:1)

Joyously; with grandeur

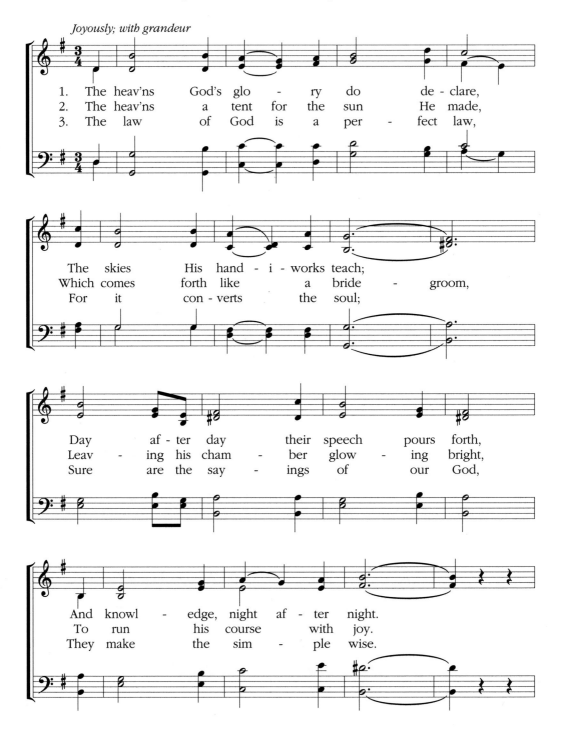

1. The heav'ns   God's glo - ry do   de - clare,
2. The heav'ns   a tent for the sun   He made,
3. The law   of God is a per - fect law,

The   skies   His hand - i - works teach;
Which comes   forth like   a bride - groom,
For   it   con - verts   the soul;

Day   af - ter day   their speech   pours forth,
Leav - ing his cham - ber glow - ing bright,
Sure   are the say - ings of   our God,

And knowl - edge, night af - ter night.
To   run   his course   with joy.
They make   the sim - ple wise.

There is no speech nor spo - ken word;
From heav-en's end its ris - ing is,
Stat - utes of God are right and just,

Their voice is nev - er heard;
Its cir - cuit to its ends;
And do re - joice the heart;

And yet their voice spreads to all the earth,
And there is noth - ing from its heat,
The Lord's com - mand - ments are pure and clear,

Their words to the ends of the world.
No, noth - ing is hid - den there - of.
And light to the mind they im - part.

TEXT: Psalm 19:1-8
MUSIC: Dwight Armstrong

The Lord Is My Shepherd

"I shall not want" (Psalm 23:1)

With tender feeling

1. The Lord is my Shep - herd, no want shall I know;
2. Through the val - ley and shad - ow of death though I stray,
3. In the midst of af - flic - tion my ta - ble is spread;
4. O sure - ly Thy good - ness and mer - cy, O God,

I feed in green pas - tures, safe - fold - ed I rest;
Since Thou art my Guard - ian no e - vil I fear;
With bless - ings un - mea - sured my cup run - neth o'er;
Shall fol - low my steps all the days of my life;

He lead - eth my soul where the still wa - ters flow,
Thy rod shall de - fend me, Thy staff be my stay;
With per - fume and oil Thou a - noint - est my head;
Shall fol - low my steps all the days of my life,

Re - stores me when wan - d'ring, re - deems when op - pressed;
No harm can be - fall with my Com - fort - er near;
Oh, what can I ask of Thy prov - i - dence more?
And I will in Thy house for - ev - er - more dwell;

Re - stores me when wan - d'ring, re - deems when op - pressed.
No harm can be - fall with my Com - fort - er near.
Oh, what can I ask of Thy prov - i - dence more?
And I will in Thy house for - ev - er - more dwell.

TEXT: James Montgomery, 1822, based on Psalm 23
MUSIC: Thomas Koschat, 1862

The Lord's My Shepherd

"...He maketh me to lie down in green pastures" (Psalm 23:2)

With serenity

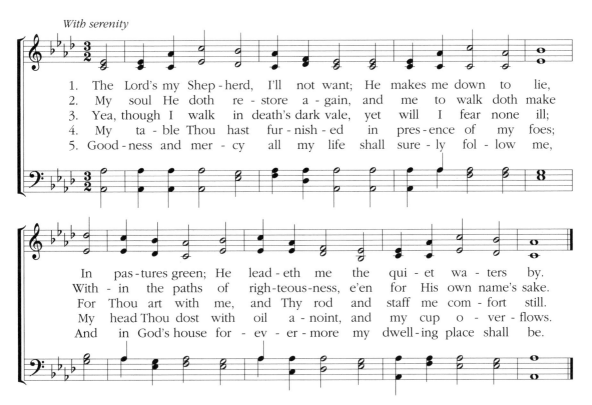

1. The Lord's my Shep - herd, I'll not want; He makes me down to lie,
2. My soul He doth re - store a - gain, and me to walk doth make
3. Yea, though I walk in death's dark vale, yet will I fear none ill;
4. My ta - ble Thou hast fur - nish - ed in pres - ence of my foes;
5. Good - ness and mer - cy all my life shall sure - ly fol - low me,

In pas - tures green; He lead - eth me the qui - et wa - ters by.
With - in the paths of righ - teous - ness, e'en for His own name's sake.
For Thou art with me, and Thy rod and staff me com - fort still.
My head Thou dost with oil a - noint, and my cup o - ver - flows.
And in God's house for - ev - er - more my dwell - ing place shall be.

TEXT: Psalm 23
MUSIC: William H. Havergal

The Lord's My Shepherd

"He leadeth me beside the still waters" (Psalm 23:2)

TEXT: Psalm 23
MUSIC: CRIMOND, David Grant; descant version: W. Baird Ross, I. Smith

The King of Love My Shepherd Is

"He restoreth my soul" (Psalm 23:3)

Moderately; with flowing rhythm

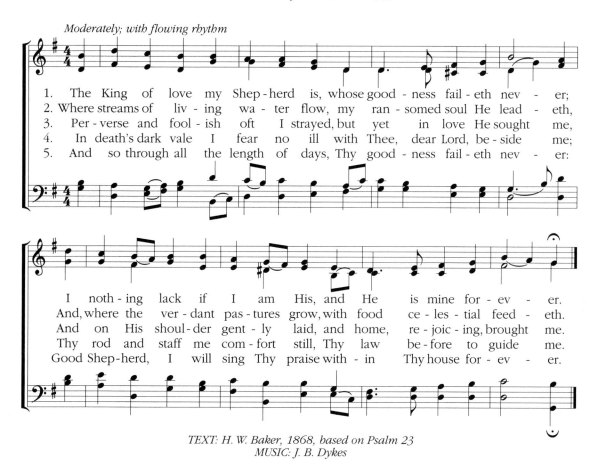

1. The King of love my Shep-herd is, whose good-ness fail-eth nev - er;
2. Where streams of liv-ing wa-ter flow, my ran-somed soul He lead - eth,
3. Per-verse and fool-ish oft I strayed, but yet in love He sought me,
4. In death's dark vale I fear no ill with Thee, dear Lord, be-side me;
5. And so through all the length of days, Thy good-ness fail-eth nev - er:

I noth-ing lack if I am His, and He is mine for - ev - er.
And, where the ver-dant pas-tures grow, with food ce-les-tial feed - eth.
And on His shoul-der gent-ly laid, and home, re-joic-ing, brought me.
Thy rod and staff me com-fort still, Thy law be-fore to guide me.
Good Shep-herd, I will sing Thy praise with-in Thy house for - ev - er.

TEXT: H. W. Baker, 1868, based on Psalm 23
MUSIC: J. B. Dykes

My Shepherd Will Supply My Need

"He leadeth me in the paths of righteousness" (Psalm 23:3)

Resolutely; with flowing rhythm

1. My Shep - herd will sup - ply my need;
2. When I walk through the shades of death
3. The sure pro - vi - sions of my God

Je - ho - vah is His name.
Thy pres - ence is my stay;
At - tend me all my days;

In pas - tures fresh He makes me feed,
One word of Thy sup - port - ing breath
O may Thy house be my a - bode,

Be - side the liv - ing stream.
Drives all my fears a - way.
And all my work be praise.

He brings my wan - d'ring spir - it back,
Thy hand, in sight of all my foes,
There would I find a set - tled rest,

When I for - sake His ways;
Doth still my ta - ble spread;
While oth - ers go and come;

And leads me, for His mer - cy's sake,
My cup with bless - ings o - ver - flows,
No more a strang - er, nor a guest,

In paths of truth and grace.
Thine oil a - noints my head.
But like a child at home.

TEXT: Isaac Watts, 1719, based on Psalm 23
MUSIC: Joseph Funk, 1832; harmony by J. Harold Moyer, 1965

This Is My Father's World

"The earth is the Lord's, and the fullness thereof" (Psalm 24:1)

1. This is my Fa - ther's world, and to my lis - tening ears
2. This is my Fa - ther's world, the birds their car - ols raise,
3. This is my Fa - ther's world, O let me ne'er for - get

All na - ture sings, and 'round me rings the mu - sic of the spheres.
The morn - ing light, the lil - y white, de - clare their Mak - er's praise.
That though the wrong seems oft so strong, God is the rul - er yet.

This is my Fa - ther's world: I rest me in the thought
This is my Fa - ther's world: He shines in all that's fair;
This is my Fa - ther's world: The bat - tle is not done;

Of rocks and trees, of skies and seas, His hand the won - ders wrought.
In rus - tling grass I hear Him pass; He speaks to me ev - 'ry - where.
And Christ who died shall be sat - is - fied, and earth and heav'n be one.

TEXT: Maltbie D. Babcock
MUSIC: English melody, TERRA BEATA; adapted by Franklin L. Sheppard

Lift Up Your Heads
Ye Mighty Gates

"...and the King of Glory shall come in" (Psalm 24:7)

Triumphantly

1. Lift up Your heads, ye might - y gates:
2. O blest the land, the cit - y blest,
3. Fling wide the por - tals of your heart:
4. So come, my Sov - 'reign, en - ter in!

Be - hold, the King of Glo - ry waits!
Where Christ the rul - er is con - fessed!
Make it a tem - ple, set a - part
Let new and no - bler life be - gin!

The King of Kings is draw - ing near;
O hap - py hearts and hap - py homes
From earth - ly use for heavn's em - ploy,
Thy Ho - ly Spir - it guide us on,

The Sav - ior of the world is here.
To whom this King of tri - umph comes!
A - dorned with prayer and love and joy.
Un - til the glo - rious crown be won.

TEXT: Georg Weissel, based on Psalm 24:7; transcribed by Catherine Winkworth
MUSIC: TRURO from "Psalmodia Evangelica"

God of Our Fathers

"Who is this King of glory? The Lord strong and mighty" (Psalm 24:8)

TEXT: Daniel C. Roberts
MUSIC: George W. Warren

To Thee I Lift My Soul

"O my God, I trust in Thee...let not mine enemies triumph over me" (Psalm 25:2)

Earnestly

1. To Thee I lift my soul; I trust Thee, O my God;
2. Show me Thy ways, O Lord; O teach Thou me Thy paths;
3. Thy ten-der mer-cies, Lord, re-mem-ber, pray I Thee,

Let me not be a-shamed, nor let my foes tri-umph o'er me.
And in Thy truth lead me Thy-self, there-in my teach-er be.
And lov-ing-kind-ness-es, for they have ev-er been of old.

Let none that wait on Thee, be put to shame at all,
For Thou art God that dost to me sal-va-tion send;
My sins and faults of youth do Thou, O Lord, for-get,

But those that with-out cause trans-gress, let shame up-on them fall.
And I up-on Thee all the day, ex-pect-ing, do at-tend.
But with Thy love re-mem-ber me, and for Thy good-ness great.

TEXT: Psalm 25:1-7
MUSIC: Dwight Armstrong

Our God Is Good and Upright

"therefore will He teach sinners in the way" (Psalm 25:8)

With confidence and warmth

1. Our God is good and up - right; the way He'll sin - ners show.
2. Now, for Thine own name's sake, O Lord, I Thee en - treat
3. His soul shall dwell at ease, and his pos - ter - i - ty

The meek in judg-ment He will guide and make His paths to know.
To par - don mine in - iq - ui - ty, for it is ver - y great.
Shall flour - ish still, and of the earth in - her - i - tors shall be.

The whole paths of the Lord are truth and mer - cy sure
What man is he that fears the Lord and doth Him serve?
With those that fear Him is the se - cret of the Lord;

To those that keep His cov - e - nant and tes - ti - mo - nies pure.
Him shall He teach of His own way, the way that he should choose.
The knowl - edge of His cov - e - nant He will to them af - ford.

TEXT: Psalm 25:8-14
MUSIC: Dwight Armstrong

Mine Eyes Upon the Lord
Continually Are Set

"...for He shall pluck my feet out of the net" (Psalm 25:15)

With dignity and conviction

1. Mine eyes up-on the Lord con-tin-ual-ly are set;
2. My heart's griefs are in-creased; re-lieve me from dis-tress;
3. O do Thou keep my soul, do Thou de-liv-er me,

For He it is that shall bring forth my feet out of the net.
See mine af-flic-tion and my pain, and all my sins for-give;
And let me nev-er be a-shamed be-cause I trust in Thee;

Turn un-to me Thy face, and to me mer-cy show,
Con-sid-er Thou my foes, be-cause they man-y are,
Let up-right-ness and truth keep me, who Thee at-tend.

Be-cause that I am des-o-late and am brought ver-y low.
And it a cru-el ha-tred is which they a-gainst me bear.
Re-demp-tion, Lord, to Is-ra-el from all his trou-bles send.

TEXT: Psalm 25:15-22
MUSIC: Dwight Armstrong

God Is My Strong Salvation

"The Lord is my light and my salvation; whom shall I fear?" (Psalm 27:1)

Decidedly

1. God is my strong sal - va - tion;
2. Though hosts en - camp a - round me,
3. Place on the Lord re - li - ance,
4. His might thine heart shall strength - en,

What foe have I to fear?
Firm to the fight I stand;
My soul, with cour - age wait;
His love thy joy in - crease;

In dark - ness and temp - ta - tion,
What ter - ror can con - found me,
His truth be thine af - fi - ance,
Mer - cy thy days shall length - en;

My light, my help, is near.
With God at my right hand?
When faint and des - o - late.
The Lord will give thee peace.

TEXT: James Montgomery, 1822, based on Psalm 27
MUSIC: Melchior Vulpius, 1609

They Are Blest Who Are Forgiven

"Blessed is he whose transgression is forgiven, whose sin is covered" (Psalm 32:1)

TEXT: Psalm 32
MUSIC: Dwight Armstrong

Blessed Is the Nation God Is For

"...the people whom He hath chosen for His own inheritance" (Psalm 33:12)

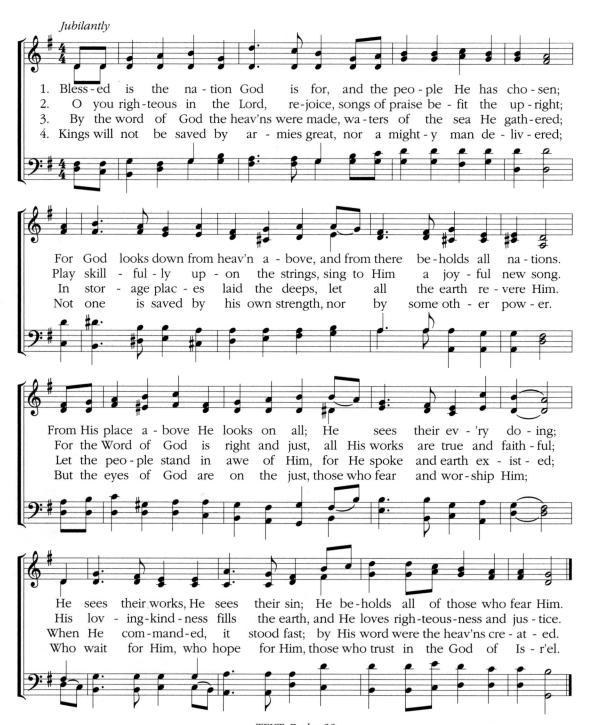

Jubilantly

1. Bless - ed is the na - tion God is for, and the peo - ple He has cho - sen;
2. O you righ - teous in the Lord, re - joice, songs of praise be - fit the up - right;
3. By the word of God the heav'ns were made, wa - ters of the sea He gath - ered;
4. Kings will not be saved by ar - mies great, nor a might - y man de - liv - ered;

For God looks down from heav'n a - bove, and from there be - holds all na - tions.
Play skill - ful - ly up - on the strings, sing to Him a joy - ful new song.
In stor - age plac - es laid the deeps, let all the earth re - vere Him.
Not one is saved by his own strength, nor by some oth - er pow - er.

From His place a - bove He looks on all; He sees their ev - 'ry do - ing;
For the Word of God is right and just, all His works are true and faith - ful;
Let the peo - ple stand in awe of Him, for He spoke and earth ex - ist - ed;
But the eyes of God are on the just, those who fear and wor - ship Him;

He sees their works, He sees their sin; He be - holds all of those who fear Him.
His lov - ing - kind - ness fills the earth, and He loves righ - teous - ness and jus - tice.
When He com - mand - ed, it stood fast; by His word were the heav'ns cre - at - ed.
Who wait for Him, who hope for Him, those who trust in the God of Is - r'el.

TEXT: Psalm 33
MUSIC: Dwight Armstrong

Turn Thou From Evil

"Depart from evil, and do good; seek peace, and pursue it" (Psalm 34:14)

Expressively; with confidence

1. Turn thou from e - vil, do what is good; seek peace, pur-sue it ear - nest - ly.
2. When righ - teous men cry, God al - ways hears, for He de - liv - ers them from fears.
3. Turn thou from e - vil, do what is good; seek peace, pur-sue it ear - nest - ly.

Up - on the just are the eyes of God; His ears are o - pen un - to their cry.
Near un - to them of a bro - ken heart, con - trite of spir - it, God sav - eth them.
God keeps the bones of the righ-teous man; not one of them shall bro - ken be.

But the E - ter - nal's face is a - gainst those who are e - vil, do - ers of wrong;
Man - y af - flic - tions that we do have, trou - bles there be of righ-teous men;
E - vil shall slay all un-righ-teous men; who hates the pure shall des - o - late be;

He cuts re - mem - brance off from them, cuts their re - mem - brance from the earth.
But the E - ter - nal de - liv - er - eth out from af - flic - tions the righ-teous man.
But God re-deem - eth the soul that's His; none shall be des - o - late trust - ing Him.

TEXT: Psalm 34:14-22
MUSIC: Dwight Armstrong

Wait and Hope and Look for God

"Delight thyself also in the Lord; and He shall give thee the desires of thine heart" (Psalm 37:4)

Expressively; with conviction

1. En - vy not nor fret your - self o - ver e - vil, law - less men;
2. Put your con - fi - dence in God, and your way to Him com - mit;
3. Cease from an - ger, cease from wrath, for all such shall be cut off;

They like grass soon fade a - way and with - er like a flow'r.
He shall give you your de - sires, the pe - ti - tions of your heart.
Wait and hope and look for God; be still and trust in Him.

Trust in the E - ter - nal God, do the right and loy - al be;
Rest in the E - ter - nal God, pa - tient - ly up - on Him wait;
Soon the wick - ed shall not be, and his place shall not be found;

So will you dwell peace - ful - ly and tru - ly shall be fed.
En - vy not nor fret your - self be - cause of e - vil men.
So shall you de - light your - self in peace a - bun - dant - ly.

TEXT: Psalm 37:1-11
MUSIC: Dwight Armstrong

Wait Upon the Lord

"...fret not thyself in any wise to do evil" (Psalm 37:8)

Peacefully; in confident trust

1. Fret not thy-self un-qui-et-ly be-cause of e-vil men,
2. Be still in God, in pa-tience wait, fret not thy-self for them,
3. From an-ger turn a-way thy-self, and al-so cease from wrath;

And bear not en-vy t'ward all those who work in-iq-ui-ty.
Who pros-p'ring in their e-vil way, suc-cess in sin doth get.
Fret not thy-self in an-y wise, it on-ly leads to sin.

For e-ven like the fad-ing grass, they shall be soon cut down;
For yet a lit-tle while and then, the wick-ed shall not be;
For e-vil-do-ers shall in-deed be root-ed out and die,

And like the green and ten-der herb, they with-er-ed shall be.
His place thou shalt con-sid-er well, but it thou shalt not see.
But those who wait up-on the Lord, the earth they shall pos-sess.

TEXT: Psalm 37:1, 2, 7-10
MUSIC: Dwight Armstrong

Let Thy Chastening Be in Measure

"O Lord, rebuke me not in Thy wrath: neither chasten me in Thy hot displeasure" (Psalm 38:1)

With solemnity

1. Lord, do not in hot dis-plea-sure lay Thy heav-y hand on me.
2. O'er my head like bil-lows rush-ing, my trans-gres-sions ris-en are,
3. Lord, my God, in Thee I'm trust-ing; Thou wilt hear me when I call.

Let Thy chast-'ning be in mea-sure; Thy re-bukes from an-ger free.
Like a bur-den heav-y crush-ing, great-er far than I can bear.
Hear, lest they a-gainst me boast-ing, joy and tri-umph when I fall.

For Thy hand most sure-ly press-es; fast Thine ar-rows stick with-in;
Loath-some are my wounds ne-glect-ed; my own fol-ly makes it so;
Lord, my God, do not for-sake me; dis-tant from me nev-er be.

Wrath my wea-ry flesh dis-tress-es, gives my bones no rest from sin.
Bowed with grief and much af-flict-ed, all the day I mourn-ing go.
To my Sav-ior I be-take me; has-ten, Lord, give help to me.

TEXT: Psalm 38:1-10, 21-22
MUSIC: Dwight Armstrong

Teach Me the Measure of My Days

"...let me know how fleeting is my life" (Psalm 39:4)

Meditatively

1. Teach me the mea - sure of my days,
2. A span is all that we can boast,
3. See the vain race of mor - tals move
4. Now I for - bid my car - nal hope,

Thou Mak - er of my frame;
An inch or two of time;
Like shad - ows o'er the plain,
My fond de - sires re - call;

I would sur - vey life's nar - row space,
Man is but van - i - ty and dust,
They rage and strive, de - sire and love,
I give my mor - tal in - terest up,

And learn how frail I am.
In all his flow'r and prime.
But all the noise is vain.
And make my God my all.

TEXT: Issac Watts, 1719, based on Psalm 39
MUSIC: From "English Psalter," 1562; arranged by Richard Redhead, 1853

I Waited for the Lord My God

"...and He inclined unto me, and heard my cry" (Psalm 40:1)

With assuredness

1. I waited for the Lord my God,
2. He took me from a fearful pit,
3. He put a new song in my mouth,
4. O Lord my God, full many are

And patiently did bear;
And from the miry clay,
Our God to magnify:
The wonders Thou hast done;

At length to me He did incline,
And on a rock He set my feet,
Many shall see it, and shall fear,
Thy gracious thoughts to usward far

My voice and cry to hear.
Establishing my way.
And on the Lord rely.
Above all thoughts are gone.

TEXT: Psalm 40:1-3, 5
MUSIC: Traditional Spanish melody

A Hymn of Joy We Sing

"I went with them to the house of God, with the voice of joy and praise" (Psalm 42:4)

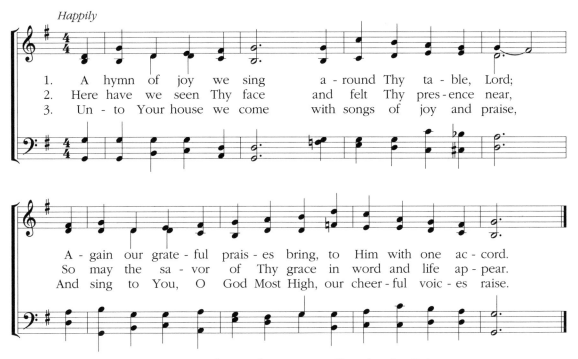

Happily

1. A hymn of joy we sing a - round Thy ta - ble, Lord;
2. Here have we seen Thy face and felt Thy pres - ence near,
3. Un - to Your house we come with songs of joy and praise,

A - gain our grate - ful prais - es bring, to Him with one ac - cord.
So may the sa - vor of Thy grace in word and life ap - pear.
And sing to You, O God Most High, our cheer - ful voic - es raise.

TEXT: Based on text by Aaron R. Wolfe and Psalm 42:4
MUSIC: SCHUMANN from Mason and Webb's "Cantica Laudis," 1850

Righteous Judge

"O deliver me from the deceitful and unjust man" (Psalm 43:1)

1. Righteous Judge, from foes defend me, who deceitful charges lay;
2. Then will I come to Thine altar, God of my exceeding joy;

God, my strength, my soul deliver, and my treach-'rous foes dismay;
And with lyre will I sing praises; unto God, my God I'll sing!

O send out Thy light and truth; let them lead and guide me still;
Why art thou, my soul, cast down; why art thou disquieted?

Let them bring me to Thy dwelling; lead me to Thy holy hill.
I shall yet have hope and praise Him; unto God shall I give praise!

TEXT: Psalm 43
MUSIC: Dwight Armstrong

O God, We Have Heard

"...our fathers have told us, what work Thou didst in their days" (Psalm 44:1)

Expressively; with conviction

1. O God, we have heard and our fa - thers have taught
2. They gained not the land by the edge of the sword;
3. No trust will I place in my bow to de - fend,

The works which of old in their day Thou hast wrought;
Their own arm to them could no safe - ty af - ford;
Nor yet on my sword for my safe - ty de - pend;

The na - tions were crushed and ex - pelled by Thy hand;
But by Thy right hand, O my Sav - ior and King,
In God who has saved us and put them to shame,

Cast out that Thy peo - ple might dwell in their land.
Com - mand, and Thy word shall de - liv - er - ance bring!
We boast all the day, ev - er prais - ing His name!

TEXT: Psalm 44:1-8
MUSIC: Dwight Armstrong

Come, See the Works of God

"God is our refuge and strength, a very present help in trouble" (Psalm 46:1)

Expressively

1. O God, our strength and ref - uge, proves in all dis-tress a pres - ent aid;
2. A riv - er flows, whose liv - ing streams glad-den the cit - y of our God;
3. Come, see the works of God dis-played, won-ders of His might - y hand;

Though the trem-bling earth re - move, we will nev - er be dis-mayed.
Tents where heav - en - ly glo - ry beams, where the Lord has His a - bode.
Des - o - la - tions He has made, ru - ins spread through all the land.

King-doms moved, the na - tions raged, and the earth melt-ed at His Word;
God has Zi - on His dwell-ing made; she shall nev - er more be moved;
"Be still, know I am God Most High; o'er the na - tions I will reign."

The Lord of Hosts for us en - gaged, our ref-uge high is Ja - cob's God.
Her God shall ear - ly give His aid; He her help has ev - er proved.
The Lord of Hosts to us is nigh; Ja - cob's God our help re - mains.

TEXT: Psalm 46
MUSIC: Dwight Armstrong

God Is Our Refuge

"The Lord of Hosts is with us; the God of Jacob is our refuge" (Psalm 46:7)

With conviction

1. God is our ref - uge and our strength, in straits a pres - ent aid;
2. Though hills a - midst the seas be cast; though wa - ters roar - ing make,
3. A riv - er is, whose streams make glad the cit - y of our God;
4. God in the midst of her doth dwell, and noth - ing shall her move;

There - fore al - though the earth re - move, we will not be a - fraid.
And trou - bled be; yea though the hills by swell - ing seas do shake.
The ho - ly place, where - in the Lord Most High has His a - bode.
The Lord to her an help - er will, and that right ear - ly, prove.

TEXT: Psalm 46:1-5
MUSIC: ESTE'S PSALTER

O Clap Your Hands

"...all you nations; shout to God with cries of joy" (Psalm 47:1)

With vigor

1. O clap your hands all you peo - ple and na - tions
2. Our God as - cend - ed with shouts of re - joic - ing,
3. E - ter - nal God reign - eth o - ver the na - tions,

And shout to God with your tri - um - phant cries.
With sound of trum - pets, the heav - ens did ring.
He rules the earth from His most ho - ly throne.

How tru - ly awe - some our Lord the E - ter - nal;
Sing praise to God, sing your prais - es be - fore Him.
And all the no - bles of coun - tries as - sem - ble,

He is King of the earth and the skies.
Lift your voice, sing your praise to our King.
As the peo - ple of A - bram have grown.

And He will choose our in - her - i - tance for us;
For God is King o - ver all His cre - a - tion,
To God the kings of the earth all be - long now;

The pride of Ja - cob, the one He has loved.
With un - der - stand - ing, sing psalms all your days.
And He is great - ly ex - alt - ed al - ways.

O clap your hands all you peo - ple and na - tions;
God has as - cend - ed with shouts of re - joic - ing;
O clap your hands all you peo - ple and na - tions;

Shout your prais - es to God up a - bove.
Sing a - loud, fill the heav - ens with praise.
Sing a - loud, fill the heav - ens with praise.

TEXT: Psalm 47:1-9
MUSIC: Ross Jutsum

Mt. Zion Stands Most Beautiful

"...the joy of the whole earth...the city of the great King" (Psalm 48:2)

In joyous anticipation

1. The Lord E - ter - nal is most great and great - ly to be praised!
2. With - in her pal - ac - es our God is for a ref - uge known;
3. As we have heard, we saw with - in the cit - y of our God,

With - in the cit - y of our God, up - on His ho - ly hill.
For lo, the kings as - sem - bled, to - geth - er they did come.
The cit - y which the Lord of Hosts es - tab - lished ev - er - more.

Mount Zi - on stands most beau - ti - ful, the joy of all the land!
When they be - held it all a - mazed, they fled in great dis - may;
We of Thy lov - ing - kind - ness thought, in Thy most ho - ly place;

The cit - y of the might - y King doth on her north side stand.
And be - ing trou - bled at Thy sight, they thence did haste a - way.
O God, ac - cord - ing to Thy name, Thy praise fills all the earth!

TEXT: Psalm 48:1-10
MUSIC: Dwight Armstrong

Give Thanks and Offer Praise

"Hear, O my people, and I will speak...I am God, even thy God" (Psalm 50:7)

1. Hear, O my peo - ple, and I'll speak, O Is - ra - el by name;
2. Sing joy - ful songs to God Most High; give thanks and of - fer praise;
3. But to the wick - ed man God says, "Why men - tion my com - mands?

A - gainst you I will tes - ti - fy, for God, your God, I am.
And when the day of trou - ble comes, I'll hear and an - swer you.
Why take my cov - 'nant on your lips, and cast my words be - hind?"

The fowls are all to me well-known, that moun - tains high do yield;
Think you that I would eat of flesh, or ask for sac - ri - fice?
He glo - ri - fies My name who brings the sac - ri - fice of praise:

I al - so claim as all my own the wild beasts of the field.
But rath - er un - to me your God, give thanks and of - fer praise.
I'll show sal - va - tion un - to him who or - ders right his ways.

TEXT: Psalm 50:7-23
MUSIC: Dwight Armstrong

In Thy Lovingkindness, Lord

"...according unto the multitude of Thy tender mercies blot out my transgressions" (Psalm 51:1)

With humility

1. In Thy lov - ing - kind - ness, Lord, be mer - ci - ful to me;
2. 'Gainst Thee on - ly have I sinned, done e - vil in Thy sight,
3. From Thy gra - cious pres - ence, Lord, O cast me not a - way,
4. Sac - ri - fice dost Thou not want, else would I give it Thee,

In com - pas - sion great blot out all in - iq - ui - ty.
That Thou speak - ing may be just, and in judg - ing right.
And Thy Ho - ly Spir - it take not from me I pray.
And with of - fer - ing shalt Thou not de - light - ed be.

Wash me thor - ough - ly from sin, from all guilt cleanse Thou me;
My in - iq - ui - ties blot out, my sin hide from Thy view,
Joy which Thy sal - va - tion brings a - gain to me re - store;
For a bro - ken spir - it is to God a sac - ri - fice,

For trans - gres - sions I con - fess; sins I ev - er see.
And in me a clean heart make, spir - it right re - new.
With Thy Spir - it free do Thou keep me ev - er - more.
And a bro - ken, con - trite heart, Thou wilt not de - spise.

TEXT: Psalm 51:1-17
MUSIC: Dwight Armstrong

Hallelujah!

"...let Jacob rejoice and Israel be glad!" (Psalm 53:6)

1. Hal - le - lu - jah, praise the Lord, praise His ho - ly might - y name.
2. Pha - raoh's ar - my drowned in the sea; men and hors - es died as one.
3. Troops of Gid - eon God did save, three hun - dred men with trum - pets cried,
4. We must fight as Is - r'el did, 'gainst the pow'rs of dark - ened night,

He it was Who showed His strength in the camp and the ar - mies of Is - r'el.
Is - ra - el passed up - on dry land and es - caped from the wrath of their cap - tors.
Sword of the Lord and Gid - e - on, Mi - dian's ar - my was scat - tered and died there.
Where - fore take the ar - mor of God and the shield of faith a - bove all else.

CHORUS

Hal - le - lu - jah, hal - le - lu - jah, praise Him, be it ev - er sung.

Ha - le - lu - jah, praise His name as the Might - y One of Is - ra - el.

TEXT: Paul Kurts
MUSIC: David M. Bilowus

Save Me, O God, By Thy Great Name

"Hear my prayer, O God...For strangers are risen up against me" (Psalm 54:2-3)

Earnestly

1. Save me, O God, by Thy great name and judge me by Thy strength.
2. The might-y God my Help-er is; lo, there-fore I am bold.
3. A free-will of-f'ring I to Thee will bring in sac-ri-fice.

My prayer hear and to my words, O God, give ear to me.
He tak-eth part with ev-'ry one, that does my soul up-hold.
Lord, of Thy name, for it is good; Thy prais-es will I sing.

For they that strang-ers are to me, do up a-gainst me rise;
To all my watch-ful foes He will their e-vil deeds re-pay;
Be-cause He hath de-liv-ered me from all ad-ver-si-ties;

Op-pres-sors do not care for God but seek to take my life.
O for Thy truth's sake cut them off and take them all a-way.
And His de-sire mine eye hath seen, up-on thine en-e-mies.

TEXT: Psalm 54
MUSIC: Dwight Armstrong

Unto My Earnest Prayer Give Ear

"Hide not Thyself from my supplication" (Psalm 55:1)

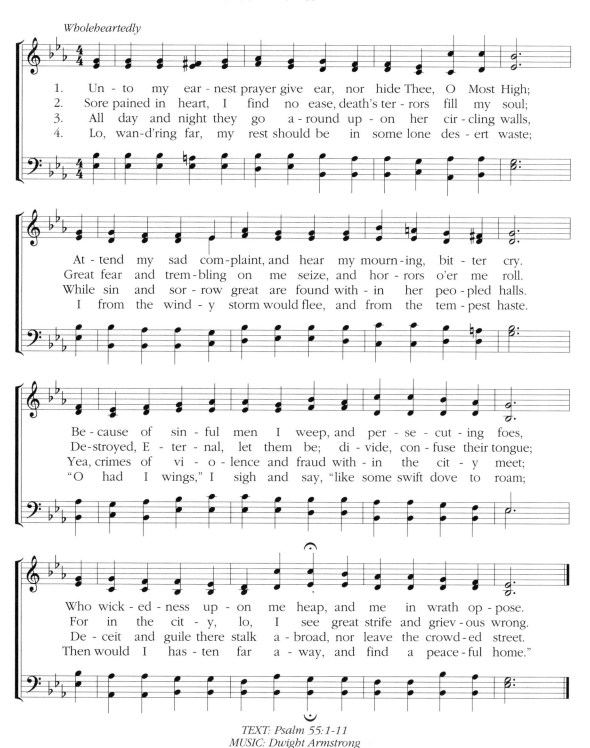

Wholeheartedly

1. Un - to my ear - nest prayer give ear, nor hide Thee, O Most High;
2. Sore pained in heart, I find no ease, death's ter - rors fill my soul;
3. All day and night they go a - round up - on her cir - cling walls,
4. Lo, wan-d'ring far, my rest should be in some lone des - ert waste;

At - tend my sad com-plaint, and hear my mourn - ing, bit - ter cry.
Great fear and trem-bling on me seize, and hor - rors o'er me roll.
While sin and sor - row great are found with - in her peo - pled halls.
I from the wind - y storm would flee, and from the tem - pest haste.

Be - cause of sin - ful men I weep, and per - se - cut - ing foes,
De-stroyed, E - ter - nal, let them be; di - vide, con - fuse their tongue;
Yea, crimes of vi - o - lence and fraud with - in the cit - y meet;
"O had I wings," I sigh and say, "like some swift dove to roam;

Who wick - ed - ness up - on me heap, and me in wrath op - pose.
For in the cit - y, lo, I see great strife and griev - ous wrong.
De - ceit and guile there stalk a - broad, nor leave the crowd-ed street.
Then would I has - ten far a - way, and find a peace - ful home."

TEXT: Psalm 55:1-11
MUSIC: Dwight Armstrong

72

But as for Me, I'll Call on God

"Evening, and morning, and at noon, will I pray, and cry aloud" (Psalm 55:17)

Plaintively

1. 'Twas not a foe who did de - ride, for that I could en - dure;
2. His speech more smooth than but - ter was, yet in his heart was war;
3. Death shall them seize, and to the tomb, a - live they shall go down;

No hat - er thus who rose in pride, else would I hide se - cure.
More soft than oil his words ap - pear, yet sharp as drawn swords were they.
For wick - ed - ness is in their home; a - mong them a - bound their sins.

But thou it was my friend and guide; we did as e - quals meet;
But Lord Thou will in judg - ment sit and bring them down to woe;
But as for me, I'll call on God; the Lord will safe - ty give:

We walked to God's house side by side, and coun - sel blend - ed sweet.
And in the deep and dark - some pit, in ru - in lay them low.
He'll hear me when I cry a - loud, at morn - ing, noon and night.

TEXT: Psalm 55
MUSIC: Dwight Armstrong

Cast Thy Burden Upon the Lord

"...and He shall sustain thee" (Psalm 55:22)

With complete reliance

Cast thy bur-den up-on the Lord, and He shall sus-tain thee;

He nev-er will suf-fer the righ-teous to fall. He is at thy right hand.

Thy mer-cy, Lord, is great and far a-bove the heav'ns.

Let none be made a-sham-ed that wait up-on Thee.

TEXT: Psalm 55:22
MUSIC: From "Elijah" by Felix Mendelssohn

Morning Has Broken

"I myself will awake early. I will praise Thee, O Lord" (Psalm 57:8-9)

With enlivened hope

1. Morn-ing has bro - ken like the first morn - ing;
2. Sweet the rain's new - fall sun-lit from heav - en,
3. Mine is the sun - light! Mine is the morn - ing,

Black - bird has spo - ken like the first bird.
Like the first dew - fall on the first grass.
Born of the one light E - den saw play!

Praise for the sing - ing! Praise for the morn - ing!
Praise for the sweet - ness of the wet gar - den,
Praise with e - la - tion; praise ev - 'ry morn - ing,

Praise for them spring - ing fresh from the Word!
Sprung in com - plete - ness where His feet pass.
God's re - cre - a - tion of the new day!

TEXT: Eleanor Farjeon
MUSIC: Traditional Gaelic melody; harmonization by David M. Bilowus

Give Ear Unto My Prayer, O God

"From the end of the earth will I cry unto Thee, when my heart is overwhelmed" (Psalm 61:2)

With devotion

1. Give ear un-to my prayer, O God, from earth's far end I cry;
2. For Thou the prayers that I did make, O Lord, my God, didst hear;
3. And in the pres-ence of the Lord, en-throned he e'er shall be;

And lead me to the Rock to rest, that high-er is than I.
The her - i-tage hast giv-en me of those Thy name that fear.
Thy mer - cy and Thy truth pre-pare, that safe-ty he shall see.

For Thou hast for my ref-uge been, a shel-ter by Thy pow'r;
A life pro-longed for man - y days Thou to the king will give;
And so will I for-ev - er-more sing prais-es to Thy name;

And for de-fence a - gainst my foes, Thou hast been my strong tow'r.
Like man - y gen-er - a - tions are the years which he shall live.
That hav-ing set my mind, I may each day per-form the same.

TEXT: Psalm 61
MUSIC: Dwight Armstrong

God Is My Rock, My Salvation

"My soul, wait thou only upon God; for my expectation is from Him" (Psalm 62:5)

Joyfully

1. God is my rock, my sal - va - tion, my hope;
2. Vain men are they, de - light - ing in craft;
3. Still, O my soul, wait in si - lence for God;

My soul in si - lence waits for my God a - lone;
Their lips they bless with, but they curse in - ward - ly;
My hope and ref - uge is in my God a - lone;

He is my fort; I shall not be re - moved;
Low men or high, both are less than a breath;
He is my rock, my sal - va - tion and strength;

He is my ref - uge, my high tow - er of strength.
Trust and re - ly not on ex - tor - tion and gain.
With God a - lone shall my de - liv - er - ance be.

How long will men take plea - sure in sin?
Res - cue shall come from my God a - lone,
Kind - ness and pow'r be - long to our God;

They plot and threat - en the life of the king.
And I shall nev - er be great - ly re - moved.
He shall re - ward ev - 'ry man for his works.

TEXT: *Psalm 62*
MUSIC: *Dwight Armstrong*

Joyfully Sing and Praise God!

"Make a joyful noise unto God, all ye lands: sing forth the honour of His name" (Psalm 66:1, 2)

With confidence and warmth

1. Joy - ful - ly sing and praise God; all the earth sing forth His praise!
2. O come, and see His great works, a - mong men how dread His deeds!
3. O bless our God, you peo - ples; make His prais - es to be heard!
4. I called on God and cried out, I ex - tolled Him with high praise;

Glo - ry and hon - or give Him; sing hom - age to His name!
He turned the sea to dry land, and the mul - ti - tudes passed through.
Give un - to Him your grate - ful thanks who has kept us safe in life,
Had I of sin been think - ing, sure - ly God would nev - er hear.

Say now to God, How dread Your works, how awe - some are Your deeds!
So let us all re - joice in Him, who by His pow - er rules;
And not al - lowed our feet to slip, though You have test - ed us;
But God in - deed has heard my prayer; bless - ed be God who hears;

So great Your pow'r, Your foes sub - mit; all the earth wor - ships You.
Whose eyes ob - serve and na - tions watch; none shall ex - alt him - self.
Though we were cap - tured by our foes, yet have You set us free.
I will de - clare what God has done, what He has done for me.

TEXT: Psalm 66
MUSIC: Dwight Armstrong

O God, Forsake Me Not

"Forsake me not when my strength faileth" (Psalm 71:9)

Moderately slow, with flowing rhythm

1. E - ter - nal God, my hope and ref - uge, Thou art my rock and for - tress;
2. E - ter - nal God, be not far from me! O God, make haste to help me!
3. E - ter - nal God, our great Cre - a - tor, Thy jus - tice reach-es heav - en;

O God, in-cline Thine ear to me; save me from the un - just man.
I'll hope and praise Thee more and more; I will tell of Thy great works.
Thou who hast shown me man - y trials, Thou shalt give me life once more.

Thou art my help and trust, O Lord; my praise shall al - ways be to Thee;
Lord, when I'm old for-sake me not; my en - e - mies a - gainst me plan;
My lips will shout for joy, O God, when I sing songs of praise to Thee;

My mouth is filled with praise and glo - ry; O God, for-sake me not!
They say, "His God will not pro-tect him;" O God, for-sake me not!
Thou Ho - ly One who hast re-deemed me, O God, for-sake me not!

TEXT: Psalm 71
MUSIC: Dwight Armstrong

For Even From My Youth, O God

"Forsake me not; until I have shown Thy strength unto this generation" (Psalm 71:18)

With joyous reverence

1. For e-ven from my youth, O God, by Thee have I been taught;
2. Thy per-fect righ-teous-ness, O God, the heav-en's height ex-ceeds;
3. My great-ness and my pow'r Thou will in-crease and far ex-tend;

And hith-er-to I have de-clared the won-ders Thou hast wrought.
O God, who is like Thee, who has per-formed such might-y deeds?
A-gainst all grief on ev-'ry side, to me will com-fort send.

And now O God, for-sake me not, when I am old and gray;
Thou, who hast shown me tri-als sore and great ad-ver-si-ties,
And I will al-so praise Thy truth, O God, with psal-ter-y;

Till I pro-claim Thy won-drous deeds to this and ev-'ry age.
Will quick-en me a-gain and bring me from the depths of earth.
Thou Ho-ly One of Is-ra-el, with harp I'll sing to Thee.

TEXT: Psalm 71:17-22
MUSIC: Dwight Armstrong

Give Judgment to the King, O God

"He shall judge Thy people with righteousness, and Thy poor with judgment" (Psalm 72:2)

In joyous praise

1. Give judg - ment to the King, O God, and to the roy - al Son;
2. Long may He live, long as the sun and moon a - bove shall shine!
3. From sea to sea, to ends of earth, shall His do - min - ion be!

The spir - it of Thy righ - teous-ness, that He may right - ly judge.
Like gen - tle rain on mead - ows green, and show'rs that wa - ter earth!
His en - e-mies shall lick the dust, His foes bow down to Him!

Let hills and moun-tains bring forth peace, pros - per - i - ty for all;
For in His days shall peace a - bound, with jus - tice shall He rule;
The kings of west and east shall bring their trib - ute un - to Him;

He shall de - fend the need - y ones, and stop those who op - press!
And righ - teous - ness shall fill the earth, as long as time ex - ists!
Yes, all earth's kings shall bow to Him, all na - tions yield to Him!

TEXT: Psalm 72:1-11
MUSIC: Dwight Armstrong

The Day and Night Are Thine

"Thou hast prepared the light and the sun" (Psalm 74:16)

With great reverence

1. The fount and flood were cleft by Thee, the might-y streams were dried;
2. That fool-ish peo-ple have blas-phemed Thy name, E-ter-nal God;
3. Lord, to Thy cov-'nant have re-spect, be-cause in ev-'ry clime

The day and night are Thine, and Thou didst light and sun pro-vide.
That spite-ful foes have Thee re-proached, in mem-o-ry re-cord.
Are earth's dark plac-es filled with homes of cru-el-ty and crime.

By Thee the bor-ders of the earth were set-tled so to be;
Leave not Thy dove un-to the mul-ti-tude of wick-ed men;
Let not all those who are op-pressed re-turn a-gain with shame;

The sum-mer and the win-ter, Lord, cre-at-ed were by Thee.
The con-gre-ga-tion of Thy poor, for-get not to the end.
Let those who poor and need-y are, give prais-es to Thy name.

TEXT: Psalm 74:15-21
MUSIC: Dwight Armstrong

For the Beauty of the Earth

"Unto Thee, O God, do we give thanks" (Psalm 75:1)

With joyous thanksgiving

1. For the beau-ty of the earth, for the beau-ty of the skies,
2. For the beau-ty of each hour of the day and of the night,
3. For the joy of hu-man love, broth-er, sis-ter, par-ent, child,
4. For each per-fect gift of Thine to our race so free-ly giv'n;
5. For Thy Church that ev-er-more lift-eth ho-ly hands a-bove,

For the love which from our birth o-ver and a-round us lies;
Hill and vale, and tree and flow'r, sun and moon, and stars of light;
Friends on earth and Thee a-bove, for all gen-tle thoughts and mild;
Grac-es, hu-man and di-vine, flow'rs of earth and buds of heav'n;
Of-f'ring up on ev-'ry shore her pure sac-ri-fice of love;

Lord of all, to Thee we raise this our hymn of grate-ful praise.

TEXT: Folliot S. Pierpont
MUSIC: Conrad Kocher

His Name Is Great!

"In Judah is God known: His name is great in Israel" (Psalm 76:1)

Gracefully; with flowing melody

1. In Ju-dah God is known and feared; in Is-ra-el His name is great;
2. The stout of heart are spoiled in fight; a dead-ly sleep the war-rior slept;
3. From heav-en God His judg-ment gave; the trem-bling earth stood still and feared;

His tent in Sa-lem He hath reared; His roy-al seat in Zi-on hath made.
No hand of all the men of might its wont-ed strength or cun-ning kept.
When all the meek on earth to save, for righ-teous judg-ment God ap-peared.

There He broke ar-rows of the bow, the shield, the sword and war's ar-ray;
O Ja-cob's God, at Thy com-mand, the char-iot and the horse went down;
Let all a-round their pres-ents bring to Him whom all the world should fear;

More ex-cel-lent, O Lord, art Thou, more glo-rious far than hills of prey.
For Thou art fear-ful; who can stand, in the tem-pest of Thy frown?
He cuts off princ-es; God the King fear-ful to earth's kings shall ap-pear.

TEXT: Psalm 76
MUSIC: Dwight Armstrong

Unto God I Lift My Voice

"I cried unto God with my voice...and He gave ear unto me" (Psalm 77:1)

Meditatively

1. Un - to God I lift my voice; un - to Him I cry;
2. I con - sid - er days of old, years of an - cient times;
3. Has the Most High strength no more? Has His prom - ise failed?
4. By God's might - y arm and strength, Is - ra - el was saved;

In the day my trou - ble comes, then I seek my God.
I com - mune with mine own heart, search and med - i - tate.
Then I think of His great works, muse on won - ders old.
Then the wa - ters of the seas saw and did o - bey.

In the night I do not cease; I am o - ver - whelmed;
Will the Lord cast off His love, and no more be kind?
I will talk of His great deeds; who is great like God?
Clouds poured forth and light - nings flashed; thun - ders rent the skies;

I re - mem - ber God and moan, nev - er close my eyes.
Is this now my lot and trial? Will His kind - ness fail?
God's true way is ho - li - ness, far re - moved from sin.
Whirl - winds shook the earth be - low; God so led His flock.

TEXT: Psalm 77
MUSIC: Dwight Armstrong

O Thou the Shepherd of Israel Art

"Give ear, O Shepherd of Israel, Thou that leadest Joseph like a flock" (Psalm 80:1)

With earnest hope

1. O Thou the Shep-herd of Is-ra-el art;
2. How long in an-ger will Thou turn a-way,
3. Thou made us a scorn to our neigh-bors a-round;

Hear Thou our prayer and Thy fa-vor im-part;
O Lord of Hosts, when Thy peo-ple do pray?
Our foes in laugh-ter and scoff-ing a-bound.

Thou lead-er of Jo-seph, Thou guide of his way,
With tears and sor-row their ta-ble is laid;
O Thou, God of Is-r'el, re-turn un-to Thine;

'Mid cher-u-bim dwell-ing Thy glo-ry dis-play.
Of bit-ter mix-ture their drink hast Thou made.
Look down from heav-en and vis-it this vine;

In Eph-raim's, Ma-nas-seh's, and Ben-ja-min's sight,
Give us Thy fa-vor, re-store us Thy grace;
No more shall we wan-der, de-light-ing in shame;

Come Thou and save us; a-wake in Thy might.
Then we shall live in the light of Thy face.
Save us, O Lord, for we call on Thy name.

TEXT: Psalm 80
MUSIC: Dwight Armstrong

Thou Shepherd That Dost Israel Keep

"Thou that dwellest between the cherubims, shine forth" (Psalm 80:1)

TEXT: Psalm 80:1-4
MUSIC: Dwight Armstrong

Praise the Eternal With a Psalm!

"Sing aloud unto God our strength: make a joyful noise unto the God of Jacob" (Psalm 81:1)

Jubilantly

1. Praise the E - ter - nal with a psalm; sing to the God of Ja - cob;
2. "Hear, O my peo - ple, hear my voice; I will ad - mon - ish Is - r'el;
3. "I am the God who brought you out, out from the land of E - gypt;
4. Praise the E - ter - nal with a psalm; sing to the God of Ja - cob;

Raise the cho - rus, make a joy - ful noise; bring out the harp and tim - brel.
You shall have no oth - er, for - eign gods; I am the God who freed you.
Hear, O Is - r'el, o - pen wide your mouth; I sure - ly then will fill it."
Raise the cho - rus, make a joy - ful noise; bring out the harp and tim - brel.

Blow on the trum - pet, sound the drum, on our sol - emn feast day;
When you were trou - bled you did call; I de - liv - ered Is - r'el."
But Is - ra - el would not heed God; they would have their own ways;
Blow on the trum - pet, sound the drum, on our sol - emn feast day;

This is a stat - ute and a law which God has or - dained for Is - r'el.
God an - swer'd in the se - cret place; with thun - der He did com - mand them.
O, if they on - ly had o - beyed, their God would have sure - ly freed them.
This is a stat - ute and a law which God has or - dained for Is - r'el.

TEXT: Psalm 81
MUSIC: Dwight Armstrong

Sing Songs of Praise to Him!

"Take a psalm...bring hither the timbrel, the pleasant harp with the psaltery" (Psalm 81:2)

Joyfully

1. Praise the E - ter - nal with a psalm; sing songs of praise to Him!
2. Blow on the trum - pet; sing a psalm; make joy - ful noise to God!
3. But His own peo - ple would not hear; they would not hear His voice;

Play on the tim - brel and the harp, and make a joy - ful noise!
He has de - liv - ered us from sin, saved us from E - gypt's land!
They on - ly want - ed their own way, fol - low-ing their own hearts.

This is a stat - ute and a law God has or-dained for us,
We cried to God in bond - age there; God heard and an - swered us;
"O that My peo - ple would o - bey, walk - ing in all my ways!

In the ap-point - ed time to keep; this do on God's most sol - emn feast!
From thun-der-clouds He an-swered us: "Hear, O my peo - ple, hear my words!"
I should have soon de - liv - ered them, turned my hand a - gainst their foes!"

TEXT: Psalm 81
MUSIC: Dwight Armstrong

Rise and Judge, Eternal One!

"God standeth in the congregation of the mighty; He judgeth among the gods" (Psalm 82:1)

With solemn reverence

1. In the midst of mag - is-trates, God His judg-ment gives.
2. Earth's foun - da - tions have been moved; all in dark-ness walk.
3. Keep not si - lence, O my God; Your foes plot their schemes,
4. Let men know that You, O Lord, the E - ter - nal One,

This He asks, "How long will you thus un - just-ly judge,
Judg - es of the earth know not, nor will un - der - stand.
That the name of Is - ra - el may be blot - ted out.
Are Most High o'er all the earth; let men know Your name!

To re - spect the wick - ed's cause, and the righ - teous blame?
God has said they are like gods, sons of God Most High;
Put them all to shame, O God, as they would Your sons;
They know not nor un - der-stand; they shall die like men;

Judge the poor and fa - ther-less; judge them righ - teous - ly."
But they all shall die like men, and as princ - es fall.
Rise and judge, E - ter - nal One, for the earth is Yours!
Rise and judge, E - ter - nal One, for the earth is Yours!

TEXT: Psalms 82 & 83
MUSIC: Dwight Armstrong

How Lovely Are Thy Dwellings

"My soul longeth, yea, even fainteth for the courts of the Lord" (Psalm 84:2)

With adoration

1. How love - ly are Thy dwell-ings, O E - ter - nal Lord of Hosts!
2. How love - ly are Thy dwell-ings, O E - ter - nal Lord of Hosts!
3. How love - ly are Thy dwell-ings, O E - ter - nal Lord of Hosts!

My soul is long-ing, faint-ing, for Thee, O liv-ing God.
For those who dwell in Thy house shall ev - er sing Thy praise!
Give ear un-to my prayer, O God of Is - ra - el;

Yea, the bird has found its home, built a nest to lay her young;
Blest and hap - py is the man, who has found his strength in Thee;
For a day with Thee is bet - ter than a thou-sand oth - er days;

O that I may find Thine al - tars, my Lord, my King, my God!
He is stron - ger day by day, and shall in Zi - on dwell!
O that I may find Thine al - tars, my Lord, my King, my God!

TEXT: Psalm 84
MUSIC: Dwight Armstrong

O Lord of Hosts, My King, My God!

"Blessed are they that dwell in Thy house: they will be still praising Thee" (Psalm 84:4)

Very expressively, with longing affection

1. O Eternal, Lord of Hosts, how my heart cries out for Thee;
2. In Thy house, Lord, all are blest; they shall ever sing Thy praise!
3. Now behold, O God, our shield, look on Thine anointed ones;

How my soul longs for Thy courts and for Thy tabernacles dear.
Blest and happy is the man whose strength is in the Lord his God.
Hear my prayer, O Lord of Hosts; O God of Jacob, now give ear;

As the sparrow finds a home, as the swallow finds a nest,
They all go from strength to strength; all appear before their God;
Better one day in Thy house than a thousand days without;

Blest are those who dwell with Thee, O Lord of Hosts, my King, my God!
God of Jacob, hear my prayer, O Lord of Hosts, my King, my God!
Better one day in Thy house, O Lord of Hosts, my King, my God!

TEXT: Psalm 84
MUSIC: Dwight Armstrong

God of Grace and God of Glory

"No good thing will He withhold from them that walk uprightly" (Psalm 84:11)

Earnestly

1. God of grace and God of glo - ry, on Thy peo - ple pour Thy pow'r;
2. Lo! The hosts of e - vil 'round us scorn Thy Christ, as - sail His ways!
3. Set our feet on lof - ty plac - es; gird our lives that they may be

Crown Thine an - cient Church -'s sto - ry; bring her bud to glo - rious flow'r;
From the fears that long have bound us, free our hearts to faith and praise.
Ar - mored with all Christ - like grac - es in the fight to set men free.

Grant us wis - dom; grant us cour - age, for the fac - ing of this hour,
Grant us wis - dom; grant us cour - age, for the liv - ing of these days,
Grant us wis - dom; grant us cour - age, that we fail not man nor Thee,

For the fac - ing of this hour.
For the liv - ing of these days.
That we fail not man nor Thee.

TEXT: Harry Emerson Fosdick
MUSIC: John Hughes

Glorious Things of Thee Are Spoken

"Glorious things are spoken of thee, O city of God" (Psalm 87:3)

Flowing; with exultation

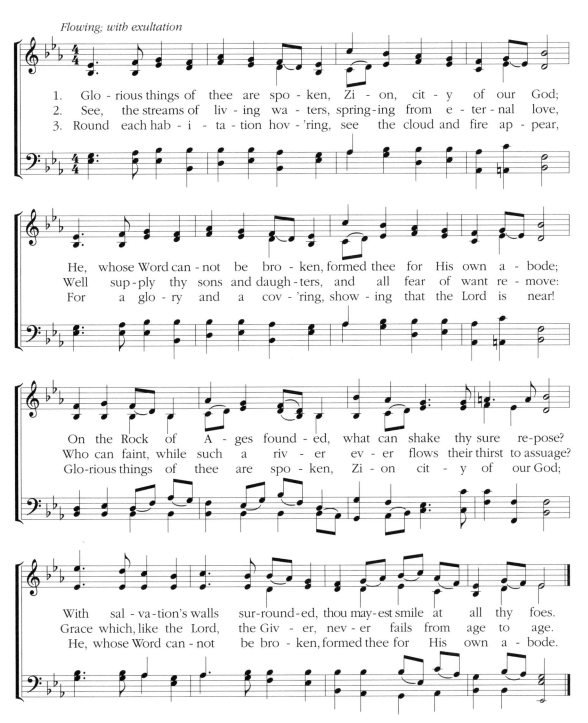

1. Glo-rious things of thee are spo-ken, Zi-on, cit-y of our God;
2. See, the streams of liv-ing wa-ters, spring-ing from e-ter-nal love,
3. Round each hab-i-ta-tion hov-'ring, see the cloud and fire ap-pear,

He, whose Word can-not be bro-ken, formed thee for His own a-bode;
Well sup-ply thy sons and daugh-ters, and all fear of want re-move:
For a glo-ry and a cov-'ring, show-ing that the Lord is near!

On the Rock of A-ges found-ed, what can shake thy sure re-pose?
Who can faint, while such a riv-er ev-er flows their thirst to assuage?
Glo-rious things of thee are spo-ken, Zi-on cit-y of our God;

With sal-va-tion's walls sur-round-ed, thou may-est smile at all thy foes.
Grace which, like the Lord, the Giv-er, nev-er fails from age to age.
He, whose Word can-not be bro-ken, formed thee for His own a-bode.

TEXT: John Newton
MUSIC: Franz Joseph Haydn

O Thou God of My Salvation

"Let my prayer come before Thee: incline Thine ear unto my cry" (Psalm 88:2)

Moderately slow and expressive

1. O Thou God of my sal - va - tion, day and night I cry to Thee;
2. Free to sleep in death's dark cham - ber, like the slain with - in the grave;
3. Mourns my eye, my pow - ers lan - guish; sore af - flic - tion press - es me;

Hear my hum - ble sup - pli - ca - tion; quick - ly bow Thine ear to me.
Whom Thou dost no more re - mem - ber, whom Thy hand no more shall save.
Lord, I cry to Thee in an - guish, dai - ly stretch my hands to Thee.

Filled with grief, my soul is sigh - ing; to the grave my life draws near;
In the pit Thy hand has laid me, in the dark - ness and in deeps;
But, O Lord, at dawn a - wak - ing, prayer and cries I'll send to Thee;

Num - bered now a - mong the dy - ing, like one help - less I ap - pear.
Sore - ly has Thy wrath dis - mayed me; o'er my soul af - flic - tion sweeps.
Why, my God, my soul for - sak - ing, hid - est Thou Thy face from me?

TEXT: Psalm 88
MUSIC: Dwight Armstrong

How Long, Eternal, Hide Thou Away?

"Wilt Thou hide Thyself for ever? Shall Thy wrath burn like fire?" (Psalm 89:46)

1. How long, E - ter - nal, hide Thou a - way?
2. What man can live and nev - er see death?
3. Re - call, E - ter - nal, Thy slave is scorned;

When will Thy wrath not burn like a fire?
Who can es - cape the pow'r of the grave?
Now I do bear in - sults of the world,

Where - fore hast Thou made all men in vain?
Where is the for - mer love, O my God?
Where - with Thy foes mock Thy cho - sen ones;

Thou, God, re - mem - ber, fleet - ing is life.
Which un - to Da - vid, Thou hast pledged.
Bless - ed E - ter - nal, al - ways, A - men.

TEXT: Psalm 89:46-52
MUSIC: Dwight Armstrong

How Good It Is to Thank the Lord

"...and to sing praises unto Thy name, O Most High" (Psalm 92:1)

Jubilantly

1. How good it is to thank the Lord, and to Thy name our prais-es sing,
2. Great are Thy works, E-ter-nal Lord; deep are Thy thoughts, O Thou Most High;
3. Good men shall flour-ish like the palm; strong as a ce-dar shall they be;

And to pro-claim Thy stead-fast love each day and de-clare Thy faith-ful-ness by night.
Fool-ish and sense-less men will nev-er know, nor will un-der-stand Thy ways.
For they are plant-ed in God's house, and they shall grow with-in His courts.

Sing to the mu-sic of the lute, and with a sol-emn sound up-on the lyre;
Though the wick-ed sprout as grass, and e-vil-do-ers flour-ish for a-while;
E-ven in age shall they bear fruit; rich and green they ev-er shall be;

For all Thy works have made me glad, O Lord, and of Thy deeds will I sing!
They shall all be up-root-ed and de-stroyed, while Thou art ev-er-more su-preme!
For our God is faith-ful ev-er-more, our Rock and righ-teous God!

TEXT: Psalm 92
MUSIC: Dwight Armstrong

O God, Our Help in Ages Past

"Thy throne is established of old: Thou art from everlasting" (Psalm 93:2)

With reflection and anticipation

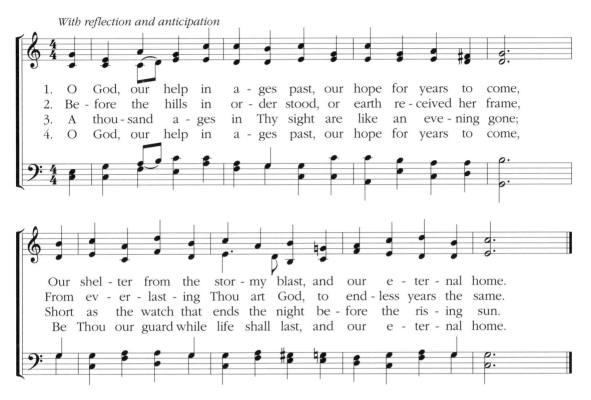

1. O God, our help in a - ges past, our hope for years to come,
2. Be - fore the hills in or - der stood, or earth re - ceived her frame,
3. A thou - sand a - ges in Thy sight are like an eve - ning gone;
4. O God, our help in a - ges past, our hope for years to come,

Our shel - ter from the stor - my blast, and our e - ter - nal home.
From ev - er - last - ing Thou art God, to end - less years the same.
Short as the watch that ends the night be - fore the ris - ing sun.
Be Thou our guard while life shall last, and our e - ter - nal home.

TEXT: Isaac Watts, 1719
MUSIC: William Croft, 1708

How Great Thou Art

"For the Lord is a great God, and a great King above all gods" (Psalm 95:3)

Devoutly; with meditation

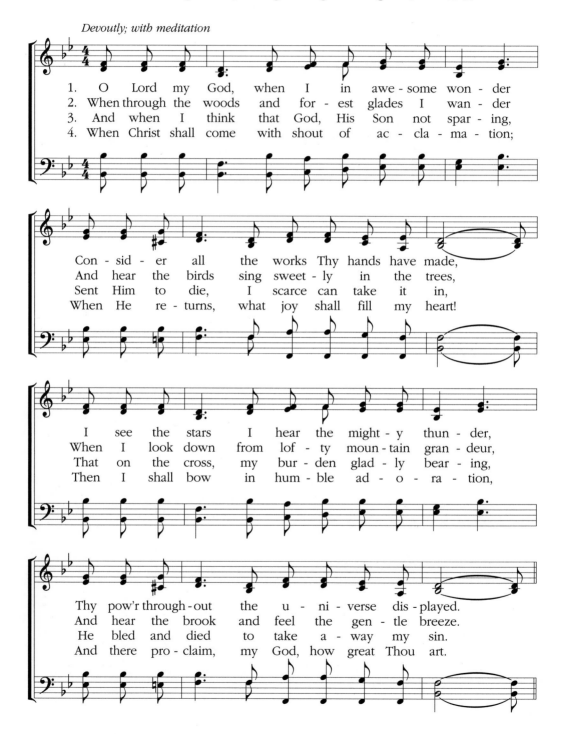

1. O Lord my God, when I in awe-some won-der
2. When through the woods and for-est glades I wan-der
3. And when I think that God, His Son not spar-ing,
4. When Christ shall come with shout of ac-cla-ma-tion;

Con-sid-er all the works Thy hands have made,
And hear the birds sing sweet-ly in the trees,
Sent Him to die, I scarce can take it in,
When He re-turns, what joy shall fill my heart!

I see the stars I hear the might-y thun-der,
When I look down from lof-ty moun-tain gran-deur,
That on the cross, my bur-den glad-ly bear-ing,
Then I shall bow in hum-ble ad-o-ra-tion,

Thy pow'r through-out the u-ni-verse dis-played.
And hear the brook and feel the gen-tle breeze.
He bled and died to take a-way my sin.
And there pro-claim, my God, how great Thou art.

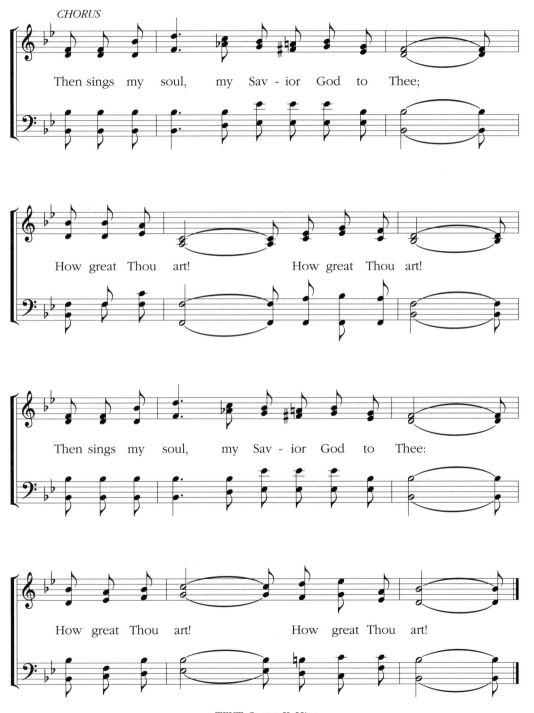

CHORUS

Then sings my soul, my Sav-ior God to Thee;

How great Thou art! How great Thou art!

Then sings my soul, my Sav-ior God to Thee:

How great Thou art! How great Thou art!

TEXT: Stuart K. Hine
MUSIC: Stuart K. Hine

O Come and Let Us Worship Him

"Let us kneel before the Lord our Maker" (Psalm 95:6)

With exultation

1. O come, let us in songs to God, our cheer-ful voic-es raise;
2. For God, a might-y God and King, a-bove all gods He is;
3. O come, and let us wor-ship Him, let us bow down with-al;

In joy-ful shouts let us the Rock of our sal-va-tion praise!
The depths of earth are in His hand, the strength of hills is His.
And on our knees, be-fore the Lord, our Mak-er, let us fall.

Be-fore His pres-ence let us come with praise and thank-ful voice;
To Him the spa-cious sea be-longs, for He the same did make;
Be-cause He on-ly is our God, and we His peo-ple are;

Let us sing psalms to Him with grace, and make a joy-ful noise!
The dry land al-so, from His hands, its form at first did take.
And of His pas-ture, we are sheep, in His al-might-y care.

TEXT: Psalm 95:1-7
MUSIC: Dwight Armstrong

The Lord Eternal Reigns!

"Let the earth rejoice; let the multitude of isles be glad" (Psalm 97:1)

Majestically; with joy

1. The Lord E - ter - nal reigns! Let us re - joice!
2. His light - nings bare the earth; men see and shake!
3. Our God is far a - bove all oth - er gods!

Let all the mul - ti - tudes of earth be glad!
His high au - thor - i - ty heav - ens pro - claim!
He is ex - alt - ed a - bove all the earth!

Dark clouds sur - round Him and fire goes be - fore;
All those who i - dols serve shall be a - shamed.
He will pre - serve His saints, those who love Him;

Like wax the moun - tains melt at His re - turn.
Ju - dah re - joic - es and Zi - on is glad!
Re - joice you righ - teous and give thanks to God!

TEXT: Psalm 97
MUSIC: Dwight Armstrong

Sing Praise to God

"He hath remembered His mercy and His truth toward the house of Israel" (Psalm 98:3)

With gratitude and honor

1. Sing praise to God who reigns a - bove,
2. What God's al - might - y pow'r hath made
3. The Lord is nev - er far a - way,
4. Then all my glad - some way a - long,

The God of all cre - a - tion;
His gra - cious mer - cy keep - eth;
Through - out all grief dis - tress - ing.
I sing a - loud Thy prais - es.

The God of pow'r, the God of love,
By morn - ing glow or eve - ning shade,
An ev - er - pres - ent help and stay,
That men may hear the grate - ful song

The God of our sal - va - tion;
His watch - ful eye ne'er sleep - eth,
Our peace and joy and bless - ing.
My voice un - wea - ried rais - es:

With heal - ing balm my soul He fills,
With - in the King - dom of His might,
As with a moth - er's ten - der hand,
Be joy - ful in the Lord, my heart!

And ev - 'ry faith - less mur - mur stills;
Lo! all is just, and all is right:
He leads His own, His cho - sen band;
Both soul and bod - y bear your part!

To God all praise and glo - ry!
To God all praise and glo - ry!
To God all praise and glo - ry!
To God all praise and glo - ry!

TEXT: Johann Jacob Schütz, 1675; transcribed by Frances E. Cox
MUSIC: MIT FREUDEN ZART from Bohemian Brethren's "Kirchengesänge," 1566

Sing Praises and Rejoice!

"Make a joyful noise unto the Lord, all the earth" (Psalm 98:4)

With exultation

1. O sing a new song to the Lord, for won - ders He hath done!
2. He mind - ful of His grace and truth to Is - r'el's house hath been;
3. With harp, with harp and voice of psalms, O sing un - to the Lord!
4. O sing a new song to the Lord, for won - ders He hath done!

His right hand and His ho - ly arm, Him vic - to - ry hath won!
The great sal - va - tion of our God all ends of the earth hath seen!
With trum - pets, cor - nets, glad - ly sound be - fore the Lord the King.
His right hand and His ho - ly arm, Him vic - to - ry hath won!

The Lord, His sal - va - tion, hath caused it to be known;
Let all the earth un - to the Lord send forth a joy - ful noise;
Let seas and all their full - ness roar, the world and dwell - ers there;
Re - joice, ye hills, be - fore the Lord; to judge the earth comes He!

His jus - tice in the na - tion's sight, He o - pen - ly hath shown.
Lift up your voice a - loud to Him; sing prais - es and re - joice!
Let floods clap hands and let the hills to - geth - er joy de - clare!
He'll judge the world with righ - teous - ness, His folk with eq - ui - ty.

TEXT: Psalm 98
MUSIC: Dwight Armstrong

God, Who Made the Earth and Heaven

"Let the sea roar...Let the floods clap their hands: let the hills be joyful together" (Psalm 98:7, 8)

Resolutely

1. God, who made the earth and heav-en, dark-ness and light,
2. When the con-stant sun re-turn-ing un-seals our eyes,

Who the day for toil has giv-en, for rest the night,
May we, born a-new like morn-ing, to la-bor rise;

May Your an-gels guard, de-fend us, slum-ber sweet Your mer-cy send us,
Fit us for the task that calls us; let not ease and self en-thrall us,

Ho - ly dreams and hopes at-tend us, all through the night.
Strong through You what-e'er be-fall us, O God most wise!

TEXT: Reginald Heber, stanza 1; Frederick L. Hosmer, stanza 2
MUSIC: Traditional Welsh melody, AR HYD Y NOS

Holy, Mighty Majesty!

"Exalt ye the Lord our God...for He is holy" (Psalm 99:5)

Triumphantly

1. The E - ter - nal reign - eth high a - bove; He is might - y, He is great!
2. The E - ter - nal One is God and King, and He spoke un - to His priests;
3. O E - ter - nal, You did an - swer them; You for - gave and You a - venged;

There be - tween the cher - u - bim He sits; let the peo - ple praise His name!
In the pil - lar of the cloud He spoke, un - to them who kept His law.
So, ex - alt the One E - ter - nal God, Who in Zi - on is most great!

He is King and He main - tains the right; He re - stor - eth eq - ui - ty;
Mo - ses is a - mong them, Aar - on too; they ex - tolled the Lord their God.
He is King and He main - tains the right; He re - stor - eth eq - ui - ty;

Wor - ship and ex - alt the E - ter - nal One! Ho - ly, Might - y Maj - es - ty!
Sam - uel al - so called up - on His name; God did hear, and an - swered them.
Wor - ship and ex - alt the E - ter - nal One! Ho - ly, Might - y Maj - es - ty!

TEXT: Psalm 99
MUSIC: Dwight Armstrong

Fill Thou My Life, O Lord My God

"Exalt the Lord our God, and worship at His holy hill" (Psalm 99:9)

Fervently

1. Fill Thou my life, O Lord my God, in ev - 'ry part with praise,
2. Not for the lip of praise a - lone, nor for the prais - ing heart;
3. Fill ev 'ry part of me with praise: Let all my be - ing speak
4. So shalt Thou, Lord, from e - ven me re - ceive the glo - ry due,

That my whole be - ing may pro-claim Thy be - ing and Thy ways.
I ask Thee for a life made up of praise in ev - 'ry part.
Of Thee and of Thy love, O Lord, poor though I be, and weak.
And so shall I be - gin on earth the song for - ev - er new.

TEXT: Horatius Bonar
MUSIC: RICHMOND by Thomas Haweis

All People That on Earth Do Dwell

"Make a joyful noise unto the Lord, all ye lands" (Psalm 100:1)

With majesty

1. All peo - ple that on earth do dwell,
2. The Lord, ye know, is God in - deed;
3. Oh, en - ter, then, His gates with praise;
4. For why? The Lord, our God, is good;

Sing to the Lord with cheer - ful voice.
With - out our aid He did us make.
Ap - proach with joy His courts un - to;
His mer - cy is for - ev - er sure.

Him serve with fear, His praise forth tell;
We are His flock, He doth us feed,
Praise, laud, and bless His name al - ways,
His truth at all times firm - ly stood,

Come ye be - fore Him and re - joice.
And for His sheep He doth us take.
For it is seem - ly so to do.
And shall from age to age en - dure.

TEXT: William Kethe, 1561, based on Psalm 100
MUSIC: OLD HUNDREDTH by Louis Bourgeois, from "Genevan Psalter," 1551

Sing to the Lord With Cheerful Voice

"Serve the Lord with gladness: come before His presence with singing" (Psalm 100:2)

Jubilantly

1. All peo-ple that on earth do dwell, sing to the Lord with cheer-ful voice!
2. O en-ter then His gates with praise; gai-ly ap-proach un-to His courts;

Serve Him with joy, His prais-es tell; come ye be-fore Him and re-joice!
Praise Him, and bless His name al-way, for it is seem-ly so to do.

And know the Lord is God in-deed; with-out our aid He did us make;
For God the Lord is ev-er good, His mer-cy is for-ev-er sure;

We are His flock; He doth us feed, and for His sheep He doth us take.
His truth at all times firm-ly stood, and shall from age to age en-dure.

TEXT: Psalm 100
MUSIC: Dwight Armstrong

We Are God's People

"We are His people, and the sheep of His pasture" (Psalm 100:3)

With assurance

1. We are God's peo - ple, the cho - sen of the Lord,
2. We are God's loved ones, the Bride of Christ our Lord,
3. We are the Bod - y of which the Lord is Head,
4. We are a Tem - ple, the Spir - it's dwell - ing place,

Born of His Spir - it, es - tab - lished by His Word;
For we have known it, the love of God out - poured;
Called to o - bey Him, now ris - en from the dead;
Formed in great weak - ness, a cup to hold God's grace;

Our cor - ner - stone is Christ a - lone, and strong in Him we stand:
Now let us learn how to re - turn the gift of love once giv'n:
He wills us be a fam - i - ly di - verse yet tru - ly one:
We die a - lone, for on its own, each em - ber los - es fire:

O let us live trans - par - ent - ly,
O let us share each joy and care,
O let us give our gifts to God,
Yet joined in one the flame burns on

And   walk   heart to   heart and hand   in   hand.
And   live   with   a   zeal   that pleas - es   Heav'n.
And   so   shall His   work   on   earth be   done.
To   give   warmth and   light and to   in - spire.

TEXT: Bryan Jeffery Leech
MUSIC: SYMPHONY by Johannes Brahms; arranged by Fred Bock

Come Before His Presence

"Enter into His gates with thanksgiving" (Psalm 100:4)

With fervency

1. Come be-fore His pres-ence with sing-ing; make a joy-ful noise to the Lord.
2. Come be-fore His pres-ence with sing-ing; make a joy-ful noise all you lands.
3. Yes, His truth en-dur-eth for-ev-er, and His mer-cy lasts for all time.

Come and serve the Lord filled with glad-ness, sing-ing prais-es with one ac-cord.
It is God, our Lord, who has made us by the pow-er of His com-mand.
The E-ter-nal God ev-er-last-ing, God our Fa-ther gra-cious and kind:

Come be-fore Him with your thanks-giv-ing, and be-fore His throne sing your praise.
In His courts sing loud-ly be-fore Him, as we wor-ship God with our praise.
He has made us; we are His peo-ple; and His sheep all fol-low His voice.

Sing your prais-es; al-ways be thank-ful; bless His name through-out all your days.
Come be-fore His pres-ence with sing-ing, as our hearts and voic-es we raise.
Come be-fore His pres-ence with sing-ing; come be-fore Him as we re-joice.

TEXT: Psalm 100
MUSIC: Ross Jutsum

I'll Sing of Mercy and of Justice

"I will sing of mercy and judgment: unto Thee, O Lord, will I sing" (Psalm 101:1)

With heartfelt devotion

1. I'll sing of mer-cy and of jus-tice, Lord, I'll sing to Thee;
2. I will en-dure no wick-ed thing be-fore mine eyes to be;
3. No man who prac-tic-es de-ceit shall dwell with-in my house;

With wis-dom in a per-fect way shall my be-hav-ior be.
I hate their work that turn a-side; it shall not cleave to me.
And in my pres-ence shall no man re-main who ut-ters lies.

O when, in kind-ness un-to me, wilt Thou be pleased to come?
A stub-born and a fro-ward heart shall quite de-part from me;
Up-on the faith-ful of the land mine eyes shall al-ways be;

I with a per-fect heart will walk with-in my house at home.
A per-son giv'n to wick-ed-ness I will not know at all.
With fa-vor shall I look on them, that they may dwell with me.

TEXT: Psalm 101
MUSIC: Dwight Armstrong

116

Forever Shall He Reign!

"But Thou, O Lord, shalt endure for ever" (Psalm 102:12)

Meditatively

1. Hear my prayer, O Thou E - ter - nal; hide not Thy face from me;
2. When our God re - turns from heav - en, then Zi - on shall be built;
3. When all peo - ple then are gath - ered to serve the Lord their God

Hear my cry and quick - ly an - swer, when my day of trou - ble comes.
He shall come in all His glo - ry; He shall help the des - ti - tute.
To de - clare His name in Zi - on, in Je - ru - sa - lem His praise!

Like grass my heart is with - ered, my days like grass con-sumed;
Their prayers He will de-spise not; their groan - ing He will hear;
All kings shall see His glo - ry, all na - tions hear His name!

My God, take not my life now, in the midst of my days.
And they shall dwell in safe - ty, for our God shall re - turn.
His fame shall be de-clared then, and for - ev - er shall He reign!

TEXT: Psalm 102
MUSIC: Dwight Armstrong

Bless the Lord Eternal, O My Soul

"All that is within me, bless His holy name" (Psalm 103:1)

With exultation

1. Bless the Lord E - ter - nal, O my soul, bless His ho - ly sa - cred name!
2. Bless the Lord E - ter - nal, O my soul, let the heav - ens praise His name!
3. Bless the Lord E - ter - nal, O my soul, let the an - gels praise His name!
4. Bless the Lord E - ter - nal, O my soul, for His love al - ways en - dures!

And for - get not all His ben - e - fits to those who fear His name.
For His mer - cy is as high a - bove as heav'n a - bove the earth.
For in heav - en He has fixed His throne and there He rules the earth.
And His loy - al - ty is to our sons who keep all His com - mands.

He for - gives all our in - iq - ui - ties; our dis - eas - es He will heal!
Not ac - cord - ing to our man - y sins has the Lord so dealt with us;
The E - ter - nal vin - di - cates the cause of all those who have been wronged;
As for man, he blos - soms like a flow'r, and his days are like the grass;

From de - struc - tion He re - deems our life, and He crowns us with His love!
For as far as east is from the west, He re - moves from us our sins!
For His mer - cy is as high a - bove as the heav'ns a - bove the earth!
But from death the Lord re - deems our life and He crowns us with His love!

TEXT: Psalm 103
MUSIC: Dwight Armstrong

Praise, My Soul,
the King of Heaven

"Bless the Lord, O my soul...who crowneth thee with lovingkindness" (Psalm 103:1, 4)

With gratitude

1. Praise, my soul, the King of heav - en,
2. Praise Him for His grace and fa - vor
3. Fa - ther - like, He tends and spares us;
4. Frail as sum - mer's flow'r we flour - ish;

To His feet thy trib - ute bring;
To our fa - thers in dis - tress;
Well our fee - ble frame He knows,
Blows the wind and it is gone;

Ran - somed, healed, re - stored, for - giv - en,
Praise Him, still the same for - ev - er,
In His hands He gent - ly bears us,
But, while mor - tals rise and per - ish,

Who like thee His praise should sing?
Slow to chide, and swift to bless;
Res - cues us from all our foes;
God en - dures un - chang - ing on;

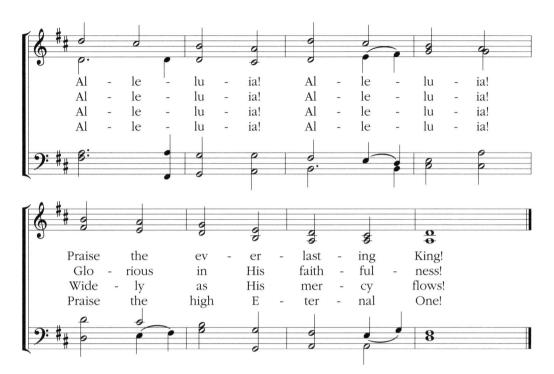

Al - le - lu - ia! Al - le - lu - ia!
Al - le - lu - ia! Al - le - lu - ia!
Al - le - lu - ia! Al - le - lu - ia!
Al - le - lu - ia! Al - le - lu - ia!

Praise the ev - er - last - ing King!
Glo - rious in His faith - ful - ness!
Wide - ly as His mer - cy flows!
Praise the high E - ter - nal One!

TEXT: Henry Francis Lyte, 1834
MUSIC: John Goss, 1867

Count Your Blessings

"Bless the Lord, O my soul, and forget not all His benefits" (Psalm 103:2)

With deep gratitude

1. When up-on life's bil-lows you are tem - pest tossed,
2. Are you ev - er bur-dened with a load of care?
3. So, a - mid the con - flict, wheth-er great or small,

1. you are tem-pest tossed,

When you are dis-cour-aged, think-ing all is lost,
Does the cross seem heav - y you are called to bear?
Do not be dis-cour-aged, God is o - ver all;

think-ing all is lost,

Count your man - y bless-ings; name them one by one,
Count your man - y bless-ings; ev - 'ry doubt will fly,
Count your man - y bless-ings; an - gels will at - tend,

name them one by one,

And it will sur - prise you what the Lord hath done.
And you will be sing-ing as the days go by.
Help and com-fort give you to your jour - ney's end.

what the Lord hath done.

CHORUS

Count your blessings; name them one by one;
Count your many blessings; name them one by one;

Count your blessings; see what God hath done;
Count your many blessings; see what God hath done;

rit.

Count your blessings; name them one by one;
Count your many blessings

a tempo

Count your many blessings; see what God hath done.

TEXT: Johnson Oatman, Jr.
MUSIC: Edwin O. Excell

O Worship the King All Glorious Above

122

"O Lord my God, Thou art very great; Thou art clothed with honour and majesty" (Psalm 104:1)

Brightly

1. O wor-ship the King all glo-rious a-bove;
2. O tell of His might; O sing of His grace,
3. Thy boun-ti-ful care what tongue can re-cite?
4. Frail chil-dren of dust, and fee-ble as frail,

O grate-ful-ly sing His pow'r and His love:
Whose robe is the light, Whose can-o-py space.
It breathes in the air; it shines in the light;
In Thee do we trust, nor find Thee to fail;

Our Shield and De-fend-er, the An-cient of Days,
His char-iots of wrath the deep thun-der-clouds form,
It streams from the hills; it de-scends to the plain,
Thy mer-cies how ten-der, how firm to the end,

Pa - vil - ioned in splen - dor and gird - ed with praise.
And dark is His path on the wings of the storm.
And sweet - ly dis - tils in the dew and the rain.
Our Mak - er, De - fend - er, Re - deem - er and Friend!

TEXT: Robert Grant, 1833; based on W. Kethe, 1561
MUSIC: J. Michael Haydn, 1770; descant by Alan Gray

O Give Thanks
and Praise the Eternal!

"Sing psalms unto Him: talk ye of all His wondrous works" (Psalm 105:2)

Moderately slow and majestic

1. O give thanks and praise the E-ter-nal; call up-on His sa-cred name;
2. O re-mem-ber all of His judg-ments, all His deeds and won-ders great;
3. The E-ter-nal's word is for-ev-er; He con-firmed His cov-e-nant;

Let His deeds be known a-mong na-tions; sing to Him, sing songs of praise.
O re-mem-ber, chil-dren of Is-r'el, He made you His cho-sen ones!
For a thou-sand gen - er-a-tions, to His peo-ple Is-ra-el.

Tell of all His mar-vel-ous won-ders, glo-ry in His most ho-ly name!
He is our God now and for-ev-er! The E-ter-nal, great is His name!
For He gave to them a pos-ses-sion, for an ev-er-last-ing do-main;

Let the hearts of those re-joice, who seek God and fear His name;
O-ver all He reigns su-preme; all His judg-ments fill the earth.
As their por-tion ev-er-more, Ca-naan's land He gave to them.

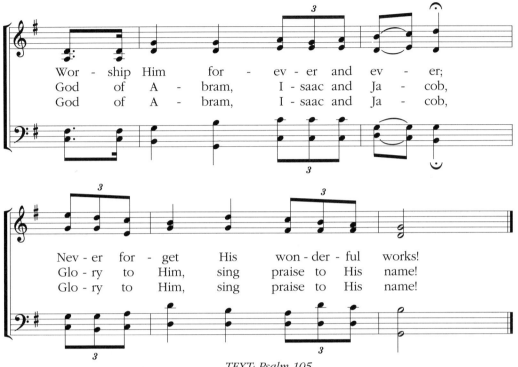

Worship Him for - ev - er and ev - er;
God of A - bram, I - saac and Ja - cob,
God of A - bram, I - saac and Ja - cob,

Nev - er for - get His won - der - ful works!
Glo - ry to Him, sing praise to His name!
Glo - ry to Him, sing praise to His name!

TEXT: Psalm 105
MUSIC: Dwight Armstrong

O Praise the Lord, for He Is Good

"...for His mercy endureth for ever" (Psalm 107:1)

With honor and admiration

1. O praise the Lord, for He is good,
2. They wan - dered in the wil - der - ness,
3. O praise the Lord, ye sons of men,

His mer - cies still en - dure;
By want and hun - ger pressed;
For all His good - ness shown;

Thus let His ran - somed tes - ti - fy,
In trou - ble then they cried to God,
O praise Him for the won - drous works

From all their foes se - cure.
He saved their souls dis - tressed.
To you He has made known.

He has re - deemed His cap - tive saints
He made the way be - fore them plain,
The long - ing soul that turns to Him

From ad - ver - sar - ies' hands,
Him - self be - came their guide;
He ful - ly sat - is - fies;

Has gath - ered them and brought them back
He brought them to a cit - y strong
He fills with good each hun - gering one

In peace from hos - tile lands.
Where - in they might a - bide.
That for His mer - cy cries.

TEXT: Psalm 107:1-9
MUSIC: KINGSFOLD, from an English traditional melody

O That Men Would Praise Their God!

"...for His goodness, and for His wonderful works to the children of men!" (Psalm 107:8)

129

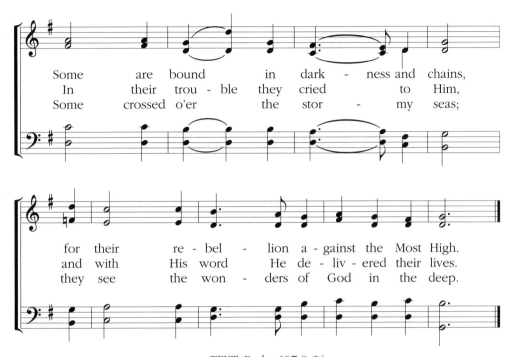

Some are bound in dark - ness and chains,
In their trou - ble they cried to Him,
Some crossed o'er the stor - my seas;

for their re - bel - lion a - gainst the Most High.
and with His word He de - liv - ered their lives.
they see the won - ders of God in the deep.

TEXT: Psalm 107:8-24
MUSIC: Dwight Armstrong

Wisdom Begins With the Fear of the Lord

130

"A good understanding have all they that do His commandments" (Psalm 111:10)

With sincerity

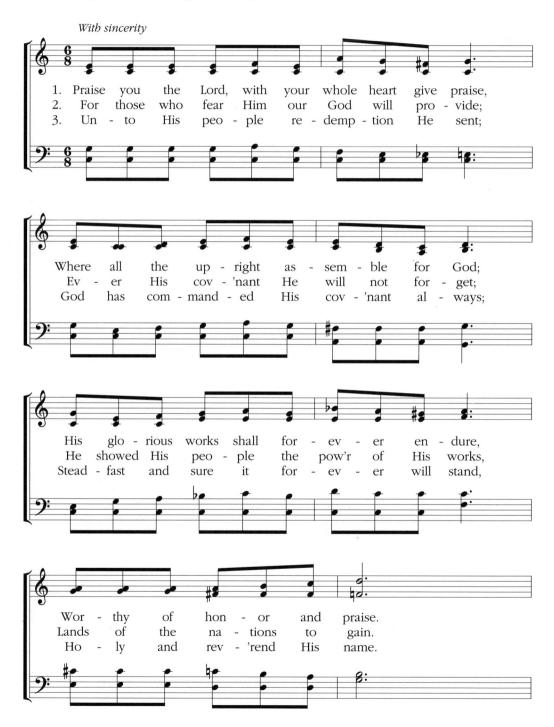

1. Praise you the Lord, with your whole heart give praise,
2. For those who fear Him our God will pro - vide;
3. Un - to His peo - ple re - demp - tion He sent;

Where all the up - right as - sem - ble for God;
Ev - er His cov - 'nant He will not for - get;
God has com - mand - ed His cov - 'nant al - ways;

His glo - rious works shall for - ev - er en - dure,
He showed His peo - ple the pow'r of His works,
Stead - fast and sure it for - ev - er will stand,

Wor - thy of hon - or and praise.
Lands of the na - tions to gain.
Ho - ly and rev - 'rend His name.

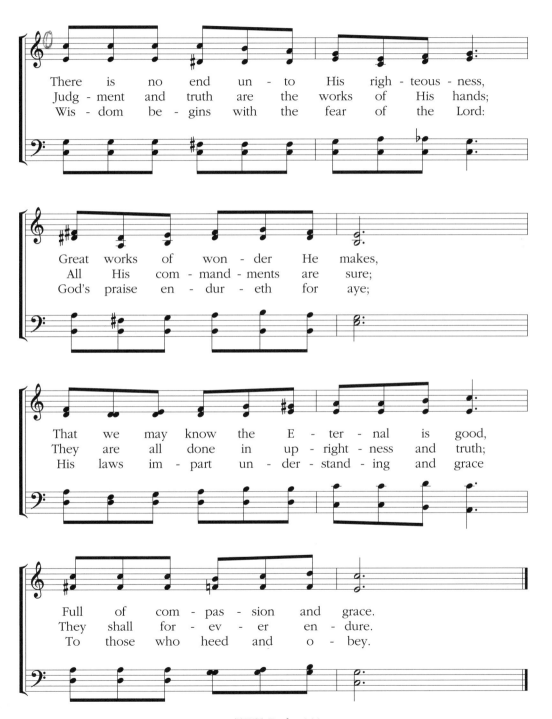

There is no end un - to His righ - teous - ness,
Judg - ment and truth are the works of His hands;
Wis - dom be - gins with the fear of the Lord:

Great works of won - der He makes,
All His com - mand - ments are sure;
God's praise en - dur - eth for aye;

That we may know the E - ter - nal is good,
They are all done in up - right - ness and truth;
His laws im - part un - der - stand - ing and grace

Full of com - pas - sion and grace.
They shall for - ev - er en - dure.
To those who heed and o - bey.

TEXT: Psalm 111
MUSIC: Dwight Armstrong

Praise Belongs to God

"Not unto us, O Lord... but unto Thy name give glory" (Psalm 115:1)

With trusting adoration

1. Not un-to us, E-ter-nal God, but un-to Thy name give praise!
2. Our God is on His throne in heav'n; He has done what pleas-es Him.
3. Men make their id-ols with their hands, gods of sil-ver, gods of gold;

Glo-ry un-to Thee be-longs, truth and mer-cy sure.
So why do the hea-then say, "Where is now your God?"
They have mouths but do not speak, ears but do not hear!

They who trust in the Lord, they who fear Him, small and great,
Is-ra-el, trust in God! He will be your help and shield;
Is-ra-el, trust in God! All who fear Him, He will bless!

He will be their help and shield. Praise be-longs to God!
House of Aar-on, trust your God; help and shield is He.
He will be your help and shield. Praise be-longs to God!

TEXT: Psalm 115:1-13
MUSIC: Dwight Armstrong

O Give Thanks Unto Our God

"Let them now that fear the Lord say, that His mercy endureth for ever" (Psalm 118:4)

With fervent praise; majestically

1. O give thanks un-to our God; bless-ed be His name!
2. I called up-on the Lord my God; in dis-tress I cried!
3. All na-tions com-passed me a-bout, com-passed me like bees;
4. O give thanks un-to our God; He has an-swered me!

His mer-cy shall al-ways en-dure; and His kind-ness nev-er fails.
He an-swered me and set me free; put your con-fi-dence in God.
But the E-ter-nal is my strength; in His name I cut them off.
He my sal-va-tion has be-come, He the chief, the cor-ner-stone.

Let Is-ra-el con-fess to God, "His mer-cy al-ways shall en-dure;"
With the E-ter-nal on my side, why should I fear what men can do?
O-pen the gates of right-teous-ness, where all the right-teous en-ter in;
He by the build-ers was re-fused; He was re-ject-ed by His own.

Let Aar-on's house-hold now re-peat, that His mer-cy nev-er fails!
Trust not in princ-es nor in man; bet-ter far to trust in God!
I shall not die but I shall live, and shall tell of all His works!
God is the Lord who shows us light; bless-ed be the name of God!

TEXT: Psalm 118
MUSIC: Dwight Armstrong

This Is the Day

"...which the Lord hath made; we will rejoice and be glad in it" (Psalm 118:24)

Enthusiastically

1. This is the day that the Lord has made;
2. Save us, we pray Thee, O Lord our God;
3. God is the Lord who has giv'n us light;

Let us be glad and re - joice.
Bless - ed who comes in Your name.
Show - ing the truth we should know.

Lift up your heads and pro - claim a - loud
Je - sus our Sav - ior of yes - ter - day,
Lamp to our feet, light un - to our path,

Prais - es, and lift up your voice.
Now and for - ev - er the same.
Lead - ing the way we should go.

TEXT: Psalm 118:24-29 & Hebrews 13:8
MUSIC: Ross Jutsum

O How Love I Thy Law!

"It is my meditation all the day" (Psalm 119:97)

With great adoration

1. O how love I Thy law! It is ev - er with me;
2. O how love I Thy law! It is ev - er with me;
3. O how love I Thy law! It is ev - er with me;

It is my med - i - ta - tion all the day in my thoughts.
I have more un - der - stand - ing than the an - cients of old.
Thy com-mands make me wis - er than my un - friend - ly foes.

I have held back my feet from the ways of this world;
From Thy pre - cepts I learn ev - 'ry false way to hate;
O how sweet are Thy words, more than hon - ey is sweet!

Thou hast giv - en me wis - dom by Thy righ - teous com - mands.
I have more un - der - stand - ing for I dwell on Thy law.
From Thy judg - ments, E - ter - nal, let me nev - er de - part.

TEXT: Psalm 119:97-104
MUSIC: Dwight Armstrong

The Precepts of My God

"I hate vain thoughts: but Thy law do I love" (Psalm 119:113)

Lyrically; with humility

1. The thoughts of van - i - ty I hate, but I do love Thy law.
2. Ac - cord - ing to Thy faith - ful word up - hold and strength - en me;

Thou art my shield and hid - ing place; my Rock stead - fast and sure.
That I may live, and of my hope may nev - er be a - shamed.

All ye who e - vil - do - ers are, from me de - part a - way;
O, hold me safe, so shall I be in peace and safe - ty still;

Be - cause the pre - cepts of my God I pur - pose to o - bey.
And in Thy stat - utes have re - spect; con - tin - ual - ly I will.

TEXT: Psalm 119:113-119
MUSIC: Dwight Armstrong

For Thy Law Is Truth and Love

"Thou art near, O Lord; and all Thy commandments are truth" (Psalm 119:151)

Earnestly

1. With my whole heart have I cried to Thee; O E-ter-nal hear my prayer;
2. My pur-su-ers come with mal-ice near, and Thy law they do not keep;
3. I do not for-get Thy law, O God; how I love all Thy com-mands;

For I keep Thy law and med-i-tate on Thy pre-cepts night and day.
But E-ter-nal, Thou art near to me, and all Thy com-mands are true;
But the wick-ed do not seek Thy law, and Thy way is far from them.

I am up be-fore the dawn to pray, for my hope is in Thy Word;
Thou hast found-ed them for-ev-er, Lord; they are val-id for all time.
Man-y are my per-se-cu-tors, Lord, yet I nev-er turned from Thee.

Hear my voice ac-cord-ing to Thy great love; save me, Lord, and quick-en me.
Look on my af-flic-tion; de-liv-er me, for I love Thy law, O God.
O con-sid-er how I do love Thy law, for Thy law is truth and love.

TEXT: Psalm 119:145-160
MUSIC: Dwight Armstrong

In Distress I Cried Unto the Lord

"Deliver my soul, O Lord, from lying lips, and from a deceitful tongue" (Psalm 120:2)

With longing

1. In dis-tress I cried un-to the Lord and He did hear my prayer.
2. Woe is me that I so-journ in Me-sech for so long a time;
3. I will lift mine eyes un-to the hills, from whence does my help come?
4. Nei-ther sun nor moon shall smite you by the day nor by the night;

Save my soul from ly - ing lips and from de - ceit - ful tongues, O Lord;
And, a - las that in the tents of Ke - dar I should dwell there-in!
For my help comes from the Lord, who made the heav - en and the earth.
For the Lord will keep you from all e - vil, and shall save your life.

O what will you get from Him? What re - ward, O craf - ty tongue?
My soul hath long dwelt with them, those who hate the peace I love;
He will nev - er let you slip; He who keeps you nev - er sleeps.
He'll pro-tect your go - ing out; He'll pro - tect your com - ing in;

Ar - rows sharp shall pour on you, with burn-ing coals of ju - ni - per.
But how-ev - er peace - a-bly I speak to them, then they're for war.
He who keep-eth Is - ra - el will nev - er slum-ber, nev - er sleep.
He will guard and keep your life, from this time forth and ev - er-more!

TEXT: Psalms 120 & 121
MUSIC: Dwight Armstrong

To the Hills I'll Lift Mine Eyes

"My help cometh from the Lord, which made heaven and earth" (Psalm 121:2)

With joy and confidence

1. To the hills I'll lift mine eyes; ah, from whence shall come my help?
2. God thy keep - er still shall stand, as a shade on thy right hand;

All my help comes from the Lord, Who hath made the heav-en and earth.
Nei - ther sun by day shall smite, nor the si - lent moon by night.

He will e'er be my guide, and thy foot shall nev - er slide;
God shall guard from all ill, keep thy soul in safe - ty still;

God Who keep - eth Is - ra - el, nev - er slum - bers, nev - er sleeps.
Both with-out and in thy door, He will keep thee ev - er-more.

TEXT: Psalm 121
MUSIC: Dwight Armstrong

Be Not Afraid My People

"...He that keepeth Israel shall neither slumber nor sleep" (Psalm 121:4)

With great confidence

1. Be not a - fraid; be not a - fraid, my peo - ple.
2. What can man do to those whom I lov - eth?
3. I will re - turn, with me you'll be for - ev - er.

I am your God who watch - es o - ver you.
What can man do to those who fear my name?
My stead - fast love, shall not de - part from you.

I do not sleep, and nei - ther will I slum - ber.
I am the Lord, pro - tect - ing you from dan - ger;
I am the God of A - bra - ham and Ja - cob;

Sons, be not a - fraid of man, be you not a - fraid.
Though the moun - tains quake and roar, be you not a - fraid.
Lift your heads, re - demp - tion's near, be you not a - fraid.

TEXT: Psalm 121
MUSIC: Sonia J. King

Unless the Lord Shall Build the House

"Except the Lord build the house, they labour in vain that build it" (Psalm 127:1)

Brightly; in moderate tempo

1. Un-less the Lord shall build the house, the wea-ry build-ers toil in vain;
2. Lo, chil-dren are the gift of God, and sons the bless-ing He com-mands;
3. That man is blest who fears the Lord, who lives and walks in all His ways;

Un-less the Lord the cit-y shields, the guards main-tain a use-less watch.
These whom in youth-ful days be-stowed, are like the shafts in war-rior's hands.
For of his la-bor shall he eat, and he shall pros-per all his days.

In vain you rise ere morn-ing break, and late your night-ly vig-ils keep,
And hap-py they whose quiv-ers bear full store of ar-rows such as these;
His wife shall be a fruit-ful vine; his chil-dren all like ol-ive plants.

And bread of anx-ious care par-take; God gives to His be-lov-ed sleep.
They in the gate are free from fear, and bold-ly face their en-e-mies.
Be-hold the man who fears the Lord! To him His bless-ing will af-ford.

TEXT: Psalms 127 & 128
MUSIC: Dwight Armstrong

Blest and Happy Is He

"Blessed is every one that feareth the Lord; that walketh in His ways" (Psalm 128:1)

With gratitude

1. Blest and hap-py is he, who o-beys and fears God;
2. Blest and hap-py is he, who o-beys and fears God;

He shall earn his dai-ly bread, and it shall be well with him.
Out of Zi-on the E-ter-nal will this bless-ing send him:

With his wife in his house, as a vine that bears fruit;
All the days of his life, he and his sons shall thrive;

And his sons 'round his ta-ble shall like ol-ive plants be.
They shall see Is-r'el flour-ish; in Je-ru-sa-lem, peace.

TEXT: Psalm 128
MUSIC: Dwight Armstrong

How Good and How Pleasant

"...for brethren to dwell together in unity" (Psalm 133:1)

With great joy and peace

1. How good and how pleas - ant for breth - ren to dwell
2. Now Je - sus was pray - ing with fer - vent de - sire
3. One bod - y, one spir - it, one Lord and one faith,

to - geth - er in u - ni - ty, so Da - vid did tell;
that all who be - lieve in His great name might be one.
one ho - ly Cre - a - tor God, the Fa - ther of all;

Like beau - ti - ful mu - sic, a breath - tak - ing view,
With voic - es u - nit - ed, to - geth - er we stand,
One bap - tis - m pic - tur - ing life ev - er - more,

like most pre - cious oint - ment, like fresh morn - ing dew
at peace with the heav - en - ly Fa - ther and Son.
one hope and sal - va - tion, just as we are called.

That de-scend-ed on the moun-tains of Zi-on long be-fore;
When we come in-to the knowl-edge and u-ni-ty of God,
Like the dew that had de-scend-ed from Zi-on long be-fore,

God com-mand-ed a bless-ing of life for-ev-er-more.
And we grow and we fol-low the steps that Jesus trod,
God com-mand-ed a bless-ing of life for-ev-er-more.

How good and how pleas-ant for breth-ren to be
How good and how pleas-ant for breth-ren to be
How good and how pleas-ant for breth-ren to be

Dwell-ing safe-ly to-geth-er in sweet har-mo-ny.
Dwell-ing safe-ly to-geth-er in sweet har-mo-ny.
Dwell-ing safe-ly to-geth-er in sweet har-mo-ny.

TEXT: Psalm 133, John 17, Ephesians 4, & I John 3:23
MUSIC: Ross Jutsum

Praise God's Name!

"Sing praises unto His name; for it is pleasant" (Psalm 135:3)

Jubilantly

1. Hal - le - lu - jah! Praise God's Name! Praise His name of Whom you serve!
2. God is great a - bove all gods; what He pleas - es that He does,
3. He sent signs and won - ders great, in the midst of E - gypt's land;

You who stand with - in God's house shall praise His name with - in His courts!
In the heav'n and on the earth, in the seas and depths of o - ceans wide;
Man - y na - tions did He strike, man - y might - y kings for Is - ra - el.

Praise the Lord, for He is good; sing your prais - es to His name!
Rais - es mists o'er all the earth; sends the light - ning and the rain;
Great Your name, E - ter - nal God; great Your fame for - ev - er - more!

God has cho - sen for Him - self, as His prized pos - ses - sion, Is - ra - el.
And in E - gypt He it was, struck the first - born both of man and beast.
Both en - dure to ev - 'ry age, and to gen - er - a - tions yet to come.

TEXT: Psalm 135:1-13
MUSIC: Dwight Armstrong

My Hope Is in His Word

"My soul waiteth for the Lord more than they that watch for the morning" (Psalm 130:6)

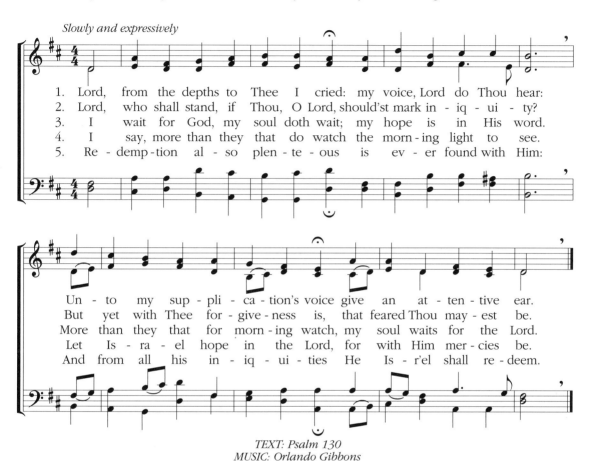

Slowly and expressively

1. Lord, from the depths to Thee I cried: my voice, Lord do Thou hear:
2. Lord, who shall stand, if Thou, O Lord, should'st mark in - iq - ui - ty?
3. I wait for God, my soul doth wait; my hope is in His word.
4. I say, more than they that do watch the morn - ing light to see.
5. Re - demp - tion al - so plen - te - ous is ev - er found with Him:

Un - to my sup - pli - ca - tion's voice give an at - ten - tive ear.
But yet with Thee for - give - ness is, that feared Thou may - est be.
More than they that for morn - ing watch, my soul waits for the Lord.
Let Is - ra - el hope in the Lord, for with Him mer - cies be.
And from all his in - iq - ui - ties He Is - r'el shall re - deem.

TEXT: Psalm 130
MUSIC: Orlando Gibbons

His Mercy Never Fails

"O give thanks unto the Lord...for His mercy endureth for ever" (Psalm 136:1)

With joyful praise

1. O give thanks un - to the Lord; give thanks un - to the Lord of lords;
2. O give thanks un - to the Lord; for it was He who made great lights;
3. O give thanks un - to the Lord; He struck at E - gypt's stub - born pride;
4. O give thanks un - to the Lord; for might - y kings of might - y names,

He per - forms won - der - ful works; He stretched the earth a - bove the sea!
For the day He made the sun and for the night, the moon and stars!
Their first - born He took in wrath; He led His peo - ple thru the sea!
He de - stroyed and put to shame; Is - r'el was saved from all their foes!

REFRAIN

Give thanks to God for He is good; He who a - lone do - eth great works!

His kind - ness shall al - ways en - dure; His mer - cy nev - er fails!

TEXT: Psalm 136
MUSIC: Dwight Armstrong

By the Waters of Babylon

"...there we sat down, yea, we wept, when we remembered Zion" (Psalm 137:1)

Reflectively

1. By the wa-ters of Bab-y-lon, there we wept and there sat down;
2. Let my right hand for-get her skill, if Je-ru-sa-lem I for-get;
3. In that day of Je-ru-s'lem's fall, when the chil-dren of E-dom said,

Hung our harps on the wil-low trees; Zi-on, yet we re-mem-bered thee!
If I fail to re-mem-ber thee, let my tongue cleave un-to my mouth!
"Down with her, down un-to the ground, e-ven to the foun-da-tions!"

Then our cap-tors re-quired of us: "Sing a song of Zi-on now!"
But we thought of Je-ru-sa-lem when we sat near Zi-on's streams;
O thou daugh-ter of Bab-y-lon, to thy ru-in has-t'ning on;

Could we sing the E-ter-nal's songs by the wa-ters of Bab-y-lon?
Far a-bove e-ven our chief joy, we re-mem-bered Je-ru-sa-lem.
Hap-py he that re-ward-eth thee, just as thou un-to us hast done.

TEXT: Psalm 137
MUSIC: Dwight Armstrong

Lord, I Will Praise Thee!

"I will praise Thee with my whole heart" (Psalm 138:1)

In deep reverence

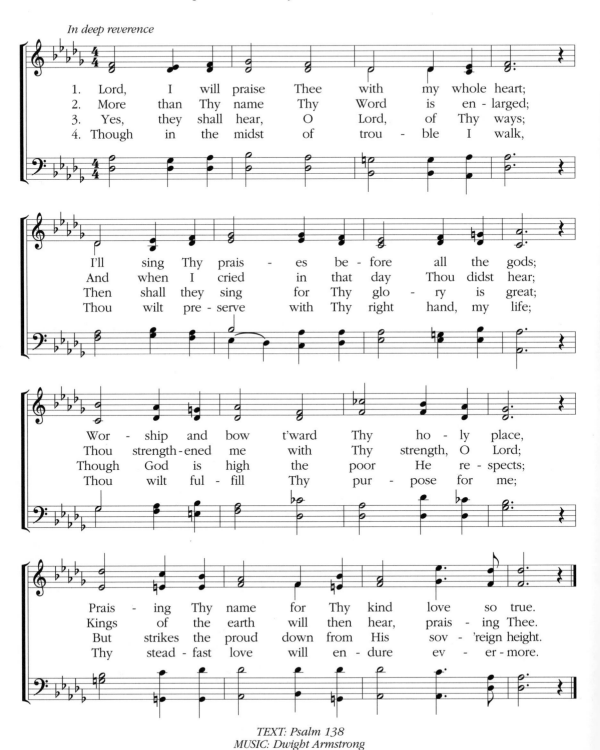

1. Lord, I will praise Thee with my whole heart;
2. More than Thy name Thy Word is en-larged;
3. Yes, they shall hear, O Lord, of Thy ways;
4. Though in the midst of trou-ble I walk,

I'll sing Thy prais-es be-fore all the gods;
And when I cried in that day Thou didst hear;
Then shall they sing for Thy glo-ry is great;
Thou wilt pre-serve with Thy right hand, my life;

Wor-ship and bow t'ward Thy ho-ly place,
Thou strength-ened me with Thy strength, O Lord;
Though God is high the poor He re-spects;
Thou wilt ful-fill Thy pur-pose for me;

Prais-ing Thy name for Thy kind love so true.
Kings of the earth will then hear, prais-ing Thee.
But strikes the proud down from His sov-'reign height.
Thy stead-fast love will en-dure ev-er-more.

TEXT: Psalm 138
MUSIC: Dwight Armstrong

Great God, We Sing Your Mighty Hand

"Even there shall Thy hand lead me, and Thy right hand shall hold me" (Psalm 139:10)

1. Great God, we sing Your might - y hand
2. By day, by night, at home, a - broad,
3. In scenes ex - alt - ed or de - pressed,

By which sup - port - ed still we stand;
Still are we guard - ed by our God,
You are our joy, and You our rest;

The op - 'ning year Your mer - cy shows,
By His in - ces - sant boun - ty fed,
Your good - ness all our hopes shall raise,

That mer - cy crowns it 'til its close.
By His un - err - ing coun - sel led.
A - dored through all our chang - ing days.

TEXT: Philip Doddridge
MUSIC: GERMANY from William Gardiner's "Sacred Melodies"

Where Shall I Go From Your Spirit, O God?

"...or whither shall I flee from Thy presence?" (Psalm 139:7)

With humility

1. Lord, You have searched and have com-passed my path;
2. Where shall I go from Your Spir - it, O God?
3. Though dark - ness comes and the night cov - ers me,

You, O E - ter - nal God, know all my ways.
Where shall I flee from Your pres - ence, O Lord?
E - ven the dark - ness hides noth - ing from God.

You are be - fore me and you are be - hind;
If up to heav - en, be - hold You are there;
Yea, e - ven dark - ness shall shine as the day;

There is no word on my tongue that You miss.
If down to hell, You would soon find me there;
To the E - ter - nal they both are a - like.

My down - fall and my up - ris - ing You know;
If I take wings or dwell far out at sea,
He knew my life long be - fore I was born;

Your knowl - edge, Lord, is so far a - bove me.
E - ven Your right hand shall hold me, O God.
How vast, O God, is the sum of Your thoughts!

TEXT: Psalm 139:1-17
MUSIC: Dwight Armstrong

Hear My Cry, Eternal One

"Lord, I cry unto Thee...give ear unto my voice" (Psalm 141:1)

With deep supplication

1. Hear my cry E-ter-nal One; let my voice rise un - to Thee;
2. O E-ter - nal, hear my cry; let the righ-teous smite, re-prove;
3. Hear my cry E-ter - nal One; tell the wick-ed of Your threats;

Let my prayer as in - cense be, as the eve - ning sac - ri - fice.
'Tis a kind-ness to de-sire; I will pray for their good will.
How their bones shall lie a-round, scat-tered at the mouths of graves.

Set a watch on my mouth; O E-ter-nal, guard my lips;
Let my heart turn from sin, not to works of wick-ed men;
O my God, turn mine eyes; let me per-ish not with them;

Let my heart not turn to sin, nor to prac - tice wick - ed ways.
I would nev - er taste their feasts; their own judg - es are thrown down.
Save me from the snare they lay; let them fall in their own net.

TEXT: Psalm 141
MUSIC: Dwight Armstrong

Give Ear to My Prayer, O Lord

"Cause me to hear Thy lovingkindness in the morning" (Psalm 143:8)

Earnestly

1. Give ear to my prayer, O Lord, and my sup-pli-ca-tions hear;
2. For the en-e-my, my foe, per-se-cut-ed he my soul;
3. I re-mem-ber days of old, med-i-tate on all Thy ways;
4. Lord, hear me, I pray of Thee, hide not Thou Thy face from me;

An-swer me in faith-ful-ness, in Thy righ-teous-ness.
My life hath he smit-ten down, down un-to the ground;
And I muse on all Thy works, all Thy hands have wrought.
Lest like un-to them I be, down un-to the dust.

In-to judg-ment en-ter not with Thy ser-vant, Lord, I pray;
Made me in the dark-ness dwell, as those that have long been dead.
Af-ter Thee my soul does thirst, as a thir-sty land, Se-lah.
Cause Thy ser-vant, Lord, to hear; show Thy lov-ing-kind-ness, Lord;

For no liv-ing man is just, righ-teous in Thy sight.
My spir-it is o-ver-whelmed, my heart des-o-late.
Hear me, Lord, make haste I pray, for my spir-it fails.
For I lift my soul to Thee; I in Thee do trust.

TEXT: Psalm 143:1-8
MUSIC: Dwight Armstrong

The Servant's Prayer

"Cause me to know the way wherein I should walk" (Psalm 143:8)

1. Lord, teach me that I may know of the way where I should go;
2. Bring my soul from trou - ble and for Thy name's sake quick - en me;

For to Thee I lift my soul, set me free from all my foes.
Lead me to the land of ref - uge, and for Thy mer - cy's sake,

Un - to Thee I flee to hide me; teach me now Thy will to do;
Cut off all my foes, de - stroy them, they which do af - flict my soul,

For Thou, E - ter - nal, art my God; lead me by Thy Spir - it good!
O Thou E - ter - nal, righ-teous God, for I am Thy ser - vant, Lord.

TEXT: Psalm 143:8-12
MUSIC: Dwight Armstrong

O Lord, Thou Art My God and King!

"I will extol Thee, my God, O King...I will praise Thy name for ever and ever" (Psalm 145:1, 2)

With joyful praise

1. O Lord, Thou art my God and King! I'll Thee ex - alt, Thy praise pro-claim!
2. To all the Lord is ver - y good; o'er all His works His mer - cy is;

I will Thee bless, and glad - ly sing for - ev - er to Thy ho - ly name!
Thy works all praise to Thee af - ford; Thy saints, O Lord, Thy name shall bless.

The Lord our God most gra - cious is; in Him com - pas - sions al - so flow;
Thy King-dom's glo - ry they shall show; they shall Thy pow - er al - so tell;

In mer - cy He is rich to bless, but un - to an - ger He is slow.
So that men's sons His deeds may know, His King-dom's grace that doth ex - cel.

TEXT: Psalm 145:1, 2, 8-12
MUSIC: Dwight Armstrong

We Plough the Fields, and Scatter

"The eyes of all wait upon Thee; and Thou givest them their meat in due season" (Psalm 145:15)

With grateful praise

1. We plough the fields and scat - ter the good seed on the land,
2. He on - ly is the Mak - er of all things near and far;
3. We thank Thee, then, O Fa - ther, for all things bright and good,

But it is fed and wa - tered by God's al - might - y hand;
He paints the way - side flow - er; He lights the eve - ning star;
The seed -time and the har - vest, our life, our health, our food:

He sends the snow in win - ter, the warmth to swell the grain,
The winds and waves o - bey Him; by Him the birds are fed;
Ac - cept the gifts we of - fer, for all Thy love im - parts,

The breez - es and the sun - shine, and soft re - fresh - ing rain.
Much more to us, His chil - dren, He gives our dai - ly bread.
And, what Thou most de - sir - est, our hum - ble, thank - ful hearts.

159

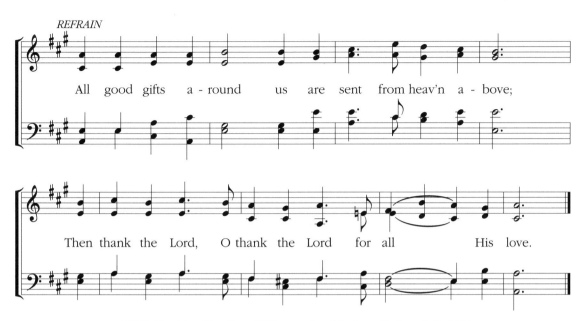

TEXT: Matthias Claudius, 1782; translated by Jane M. Campbell, 1861
MUSIC: Johann A. P. Schultz, 1809; harmonized by J. B. Dykes

Hallelujah! Praise God!

"Praise ye the Lord...I will sing praises unto my God" (Psalm 146:1, 2)

Joyously

1. Sing un-to the E-ter-nal; sing your prais-es to Him;
2. Sing un-to the E-ter-nal; give your prais-es to Him;
3. Sing un-to the E-ter-nal; let your hope be in Him;

Put your trust not in mor-tals, for in them is no help.
He it was who made heav-en, earth and sea and all things.
He re-mains true for-ev-er; He gives jus-tice to all.

CHORUS

Hal-le-lu-jah! Praise God! The E-ter-nal shall reign!

He shall reign for all a-ges, our King and our God!

TEXT: Psalm 146
MUSIC: Dwight Armstrong

Praise Ye the Lord, the Almighty

"Let every thing that hath breath praise the Lord" (Psalm 150:6)

With adoration

1. Praise ye the Lord, the Al-might-y, the King of cre-a - tion!
2. Praise ye the Lord, who o'er all things so won-drous-ly reign - eth,
3. Praise ye the Lord, who with mar-vel-ous wis-dom hath made thee!
4. Praise ye the Lord, O let all that is in me a-dore Him!

O my soul, praise Him, for He is thy health and sal-va - tion!
Shel-ters thee un-der His wings, yea, so gent-ly sus-tain - eth!
Decked thee with health, and with lov-ing hand guid-ed and stayed thee;
All that hath life and breath, come now with prais-es be-fore Him!

All ye who hear, now to His tem-ple draw near;
Hast thou not seen how thy de-sires e'er have been
How oft in grief hath not He brought thee re - lief,
Let the A - men sound from His peo-ple a - gain:

Join me in glad ad-o-ra - tion!
Grant-ed in what He or-dain - eth?
Spread-ing His wings for to shade thee?
Glad-ly for aye we a-dore Him.

TEXT: Joachim Neander
MUSIC: LOBE DEN HERREN

All Creatures of Our God and King

"Let them praise the name of the Lord: for His name alone is excellent" (Psalm 148:13)

With joyous adoration

1. All crea-tures of our God and King,
2. Thou rush-ing wind that art so strong,
3. Thou flow-ing wa-ter, pure and clear,
4. And all ye men of ten-der heart,

Lift up your voice and with us sing,
Ye clouds that sail in heav'n a-long,
Make mu-sic for thy Lord to hear,
For-giv-ing oth-ers, take your part,

Al-le-lu-ia, Al-le-lu-ia!
O praise Him, Al-le-lu-ia!
Al-le-lu-ia, Al-le-lu-ia!
O sing ye Al-le-lu-ia!

Thou burn-ing sun with gold-en beam,
Thou ris-ing morn, in praise re-joice,
Thou fire so mas-ter-ful and bright,
Ye who long pain and sor-row bear,

Thou   sil - ver moon with soft - er gleam,
Ye   lights of   eve - ning, find   a   voice;
That   giv - est man both warmth and light,
Praise   God   and   on   Him cast your care;

O praise Him,   O   praise Him, Al - le - lu - ia,

Al - le - lu - ia,   Al - le - lu - ia!

TEXT: Francis of Assisi; translated by William H. Draper
MUSIC: LASST UNS ERFREUEN, arr. Ralph Vaughan Williams; from "Geistliche Kirchengesänge"

Praise Ye the Lord!

"His name alone is excellent; His glory is above the earth and heaven" (Psalm 148:13)

With jubilant reverence

1. Praise ye the Lord! Praise ye the Lord!
2. Praise ye the Lord! Ye mam - mals and deeps, too,
3. Praise ye the Lord! Praise ye the Lord!

Praise from the heav - ens and praise in the heights!
Fire, hail and wind - storms ful - fill - ing His word!
Praise from the heav - ens and praise in the heights!

Praise Him, ye an - gels, praise Him, ye hosts, O
Va - pors and snow, all hills, too, and moun - tains, all
Praise Him, ye an - gels, praise Him, ye hosts, for His

praise Him, ye sun, moon and stars in the heights!
ce - dars and fruit trees, let all praise His name!
glo - ry is high - er than heav - en a - bove.

TEXT: Psalm 148
MUSIC: Dwight Armstrong

166

Train Up a Child

"...in the way he should go: and when he is old, he will not depart from it" (Proverbs 22:6)

With tender feeling

1. Train up a child in the way he should go;
2. Chil - dren should hon - or their par - ents as well,
D.C. Train up a child in the way he should go;

When he is old - er, he will not de - part.
Claim - ing the prom - ise made prior to their birth.
When he is old - er, he will not de - part.

Nur - ture, ad - mon - ish and bring him up wise - ly;
All may be well and you'll flour - ish and pros - per,
Nur - ture, ad - mon - ish and bring him up wise - ly;

Fine

When he grows up, he will glad - den your heart.
Long live your life, all your days on the earth.
When he grows up, he will glad - den your heart.

Fa - thers, pro - voke not your chil - dren to an - ger;
Wise sons and daugh - ters, hear fa - thers' in - struc - tion;

Give them the time they so des - p'rate - ly need.
Lis - ten in - tent - ly to moth - ers' ad - vice.

Guide and di - rect in the ways of our Sav - ior;
Learn by the bit - ter ex - pe - rience of oth - ers;

D.C. al Fine

Give them your love; you'll be bless - ed in - deed.
God wants to give you a full, hap - py life.

TEXT: Proverbs 13:1, 22:6, John 10:10 & Ephesians 6:1-4
MUSIC: Ross Jutsum

Joy to the Heart

"Ointment and perfume rejoice the heart: so doth the sweetness of a man's friend" (Proverbs 27:9)

Devotedly

1. Trea - sure your friend - ship and hon - or the Lord;
2. True friends be - side you will al - ways be there;
3. Good friends speak of - ten as one to an - oth - er;

Love from our friends in our hearts ev - er stored.
Good times and bad times through joy and de - spair.
Christ hears the words of His sis - ters and broth - ers.

Al - ways take time to be lov - ing and share;
If one should fall, then true friends lend a hand;
Prom - ised re - mem - brance for liv - ing His way,

That's when a friend shows how much that he cares.
Lift and en - cour - age and help un - der - stand.
God makes His trea - sure and jewels on that day.

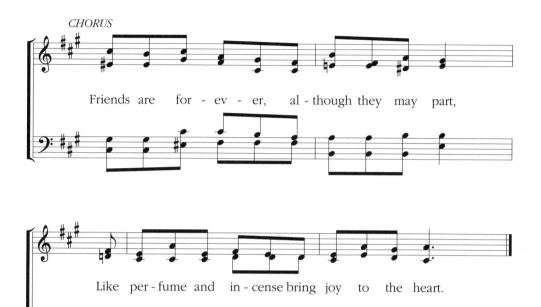

CHORUS

Friends are for - ev - er, al - though they may part,

Like per - fume and in - cense bring joy to the heart.

TEXT: *Proverbs 27:9, Ecclesiastes 4:10 & Malachi 3:16-17*
MUSIC: Ross Jutsum

Who Can Find a Virtuous Woman?

"...for her price is far above rubies" (Proverbs 31:10)

Reflectively

1. Who can find a vir-tu-ous wom-an?
2. Who can find a vir-tu-ous wom-an?
3. Who can find a vir-tu-ous wom-an?
4. Who can find a vir-tu-ous wom-an?

She's worth more than gems of great price.
Wool and flax she seeks for her work.
Bring-ing food like ships from a-far.
Help-ful kind-ness guides all her words.

Trust is hers from the heart of her hus-band;
Will-ing-ly bus-y, her hands hold the dis-taff;
Ear-ly she ris-es and serves a warm break-fast;
Hon-or and strength give her cause for re-joic-ing.

She does him well each day of her life.
All plain-ly see her prod-uct is good.
Plan-ning the day with lov-ing con-cern.
Hus-band and child give praise that is due.

Fa - vor's de - ceit - ful; beau - ty is vain.
Cloth - ing her fam - 'ly, dress - ing them well,
Day - break to night - fall, ev - 'ry day counts;
Fa - vor's de - ceit - ful, beau - ty is vain.

She shall be praised who fears the Lord.
She is pre - pared for win - ter and cold.
Meet - ing each chal - lenge find - ing suc - cess.
She shall be praised who fears the Lord.

Give her the fruits of her own la - bor;
Her gen - 'rous spir - it reach - es the need - y;
Plan - ning a vine - yard, sell - ing to mer - chants,
Give her the fruits of her own la - bor;

Yes, let her works give her praise in the gates.
Man - y do well, but she ex - cels all.
Serv - ing her fam - 'ly in ev - 'ry re - spect.
Yes, let her works give her praise in the gates.

TEXT: Proverbs 31
MUSIC: Ruth Myrick

All Your Might

"Whatever your hand finds to do..." (Ecclesiastes 9:10)

With determination

1. What - ev - er your hand finds to do, do it with all your might;
2. Re - joice O young man in your youth, let your heart fill with cheer;

What - ev - er is law - ful and true, do it with - in God's sight.
Re - mem - ber His Word is the truth, al - ways to Him draw near.

Fine

The chal - lenge is not to the rich, nor to strong the bat - tle call;
The works of the righ - teous and wise, they are al - ways in God's way;

D.C. al fine (both verses)

Rich - es are not to the wise, time and chance will touch them all.
Wise men pos - sess the good land, they shall pros - per all their days.

TEXT: Ecclesiastes 9:10-11, 11:9
MUSIC: Ross Jutsum

Remember Your Creator

"...in the days of your youth" (Ecclesiastes 12:1)

Earnestly

1. Re - mem - ber your Cre - a - tor, in the days of your youth,
2. All sons and daugh - ters lis - ten; by His laws we should live,
3. Now all these things are writ - ten as ex - am - ples for you,
4. Re - mem - ber your Cre - a - tor, in the days of your youth,

Be - fore the time of trou - ble will ap - pear.
And write them on the ta - ble of our hearts.
With ev - 'ry word in - spired for our good.
Be - fore the time of trou - ble will ap - pear.

Re - mem - ber your Cre - a - tor, He's the au - thor of all truth.
To all the house of Is - r'el, it's the cov - e - nant He gives.
So live as God com - mand - ed, let no man de - spise your youth.
Re - mem - ber your Cre - a - tor, He's the au - thor of all truth.

Re - mem - ber now, be - fore the years draw near.
He'll be our God; we'll nev - er be a - part.
And live your life as God has said we should.
Re - mem - ber now, be - fore the years draw near.

TEXT: Proverbs 7:1-3, I Corinthians 10:11, I Timothy 4:12, II Timothy 3:16 & Hebrews 8:10
MUSIC: Ross Jutsum

Won't It Be Great!

"...and they shall beat their swords into plowshares" (Isaiah 2:4)

Enthusiastically

Won't it be great in the world to-mor-row
Won't it be great in the world to-mor-row
Won't it be great in the world to-mor-row
Won't it be great in the world to-mor-row

when the earth will be at peace.
with no wor - ries and no fears.
when the earth will be at peace.
with no wor - ries and no fears.

Won't it be great when there's no more sor - row,
Won't it be great when there's no more sor - row,
Won't it be great when there's no more sor - row,
Won't it be great when there's no more sor - row,

Fine

and all suf – fer – ing will cease.
and God wipes a - way all tears.
and all suf – fer – ing will cease.
and God wipes a - way all tears.

TEXT: Isaiah 2:4
MUSIC: Ross Jutsum

The Mighty Prince of Peace

"Wonderful Counselor, Mighty God, Everlasting Father, Prince of Peace" (Isaiah 9:6)

Triumphantly

1. Up - on a horse of bril - liant white, our Lord the King re - turns;
2. Come let us go up to the mount, the moun - tain of the Lord;
3. And then we'll see a great new heav'n, no death, no tears or pain,

He comes with peace and hap - pi - ness; His love we all shall learn.
For He shall judge with righ - teous - ness and with His might - y sword.
And all the earth will be made new when Je - sus Christ will reign.

With glo - ry, truth and faith - ful - ness, the root of Jes - se comes.
He'll teach all na - tions of His law, of walk - ing in His ways.
The Ho - ly Cit - y from the sky, Je - ru - sa - lem will come,

He rules with grace and mer - cy, and the liv - ing wa - ters run.
For out of Zi - on shall go forth our thank - ful - ness and praise.
The tab - er - na - cle of our God, and Je - sus Christ His Son.

TEXT: Isaiah 9:6
MUSIC: Ross Jutsum

The Word of God Shall Stand

"The grass withereth, the flower fadeth: but the Word of our God shall stand for ever" (Isaiah 40:8)

With unshakable confidence

1. The Word of God is pow-er-ful and sharp-er than a sword,
2. The Word of God is near to you, it's in your mouth and heart.
3. The Al-pha and O-me-ga, be-gin-ning and the end;

Di-vid-ing soul and spir-it by the teach-ings of the Lord.
The spir-it's sword by which we live, it nev-er shall de-part.
The first and last, a-bid-ing truth, on which we can de-pend.

Dis-cern-er of the heart's in-tents, it's heard through-out the land.
By stud-y show your-self ap-proved, a work-man, not a-shamed;
Foun-da-tion of all knowl-edge whose ev-'ry word is pure;

The flow-ers and the grass do fade, but the Word of God shall stand.
To un-der-stand the Word of truth, up-hold His ho-ly name.
The Word of God will nev-er die; it shall al-ways en-dure.

TEXT: Deuteronomy 30:14, Ephesians 6:17, II Timothy 2:15, I Peter 1:23, 25 & Revelation 22:13
MUSIC: Ross Jutsum

Joyful, Joyful, We Adore Thee

"Sing, O heavens; and be joyful, O earth" (Isaiah 49:13)

1. Joy - ful, joy - ful, we a - dore Thee, God of glo - ry, Lord of love;
2. All Thy works with joy sur - round Thee; earth and heav'n re - flect Thy rays;
3. Thou art giv - ing and for - giv - ing, ev - er bless - ing, ev - er blest,
4. Mor - tals, join the hap - py cho - rus which the morn - ing stars be - gan;

Hearts un - fold like flow'rs be - fore Thee, op - 'ning to the sun a - bove.
Stars and an - gels sing a - round Thee, cen - ter of un - bro - ken praise.
Well-spring of the joy of liv - ing, o - cean depth of hap - py rest!
Fa - ther love is reign - ing o'er us; broth - er love binds man to man.

Melt the clouds of sin and sad - ness; drive the dark of doubt a - way;
Field and for - est, vale and moun - tain, flow - 'ry mead - ow, flash - ing sea,
Thou our Fa - ther, Christ our Broth - er, all who live in love are Thine;
Ev - er sing - ing, march we on - ward, vic - tors in the midst of strife,

Giv - er of im - mor - tal glad - ness, fill us with the light of day.
Chant - ing bird and flow - ing foun - tain, call us to re - joice in Thee.
Teach us how to love each oth - er; lift us to the joy di - vine.
Joy - ful mu - sic leads us sun - ward in the tri - umph song of life.

TEXT: Henry van Dyke
MUSIC: Ludwig van Beethoven; melody from Ninth Symphony; adapted by Edward Hodges

We've a Story to Tell to the Nations

"Then shall thy light rise in obscurity, and thy darkness be as the noon day" (Isaiah 58:10)

Enthusiastically

1. We've a sto - ry to tell to the na - tions
2. We've a song to be sung to the na - tions
3. We've a mes - sage to give to the na - tions

That shall turn their hearts to the right,
That shall lift their hearts to the Lord,
That the Lord who reign - eth a - bove

A sto - ry of truth and mer - cy,
A song that shall con - quer e - vil,
Hath sent us His Son to save us,

A sto - ry of peace and light,
And shat - ter the spear and sword,
And show us that God is love,

A sto - ry of peace and light.
And shat - ter the spear and sword.
And show us that God is love.

CHORUS

For the dark - ness shall turn to dawn - ing,

And the dawn - ing to noon day bright,

And Christ's great King - dom shall come to earth,

The King - dom of love and light.

TEXT: Colin Sterne
MUSIC: Adapted from H. Ernest Nichol

Celebration of Life

"Be ye glad and rejoice for ever in that which I create" (Isaiah 65:18)

Exuberantly

1. O wor-thy are You of glo-ry and hon-or.
2. And with Your great hands, You made man and wom-an.
3. Be-hold God will make new earth and new heav-ens.

O praise to Your name, our God the Cre-a-tor.
And in Your great im - age You did cre-ate them.
And He will cre-ate a new heart in all men.

You cre-at - ed the sun, You cre-at - ed the earth,
For You gave to them life, and You gave to them earth,
So be glad and re - joice, for the world He'll cre - ate,

You cre-at - ed the won - der-ful u - ni - verse.
And You gave them the won - der-ful u - ni - verse.
For the peace and the joy, and the weep - ing no more.

CHORUS

Let's cel - e-brate life, let's sing to Him,

Give hon - or and glo - ry to God a - bove.

Let's cel - e-brate life, let's sing to Him,

Give hon - or and praise to our God of love.

TEXT: Genesis 1:1, 27 & Isaiah 65:17-19
MUSIC: Sarah S. Bilowus

There Is a Balm in Gilead

"Go up into Gilead, and take balm" (Jeremiah 46:11)

With faith and serenity

There is a balm in Gil - e - ad to make the wound - ed whole;

There is a balm in Gil - e - ad to heal the sin - sick soul.

Fine

Some-times I feel dis - cour - aged, and think my work's in vain,
If you can't preach like Pe - ter, if you can't pray like Paul,

D.C. al Fine

But then the Ho - ly Spir - it re - vives my soul a - gain.
Just tell the love of Je - sus, and say He died for all.

TEXT: Jeremiah 46:11
MUSIC: Traditional Spiritual

Eternal Father, Strong to Save

"Their Redeemer is strong; the Lord of Hosts is His name" (Jeremiah 50:34)

Prayerfully

1. E - ter - nal Fa - ther, strong to save, Whose arm hath bound the rest - less wave,
2. O Christ, the Lord of hill and plain o'er which our traf - fic runs a - main,
3. O Spir - it, whom the Fa - ther sent to spread a - broad the fir - ma - ment,

Who bids the might - y o - cean deep its own ap - point - ed lim - its keep:
By moun - tain pass or val - ley low: Wher - ev - er, Lord, our breth - ren go,
O Wind of heav - en, by Thy might save all who dare the ea - gle's flight,

O hear us when we cry to Thee for those in per - il on the sea.
Pro - tect them by Thy guard - ing hand from ev - 'ry per - il on the land.
And keep them by Thy watch - ful care from ev - 'ry per - il in the air.

TEXT: William Whiting, stanza 1; Robert Nelson Spencer, stanzas 2, 3
MUSIC: John Bacchus Dykes

Great Is Thy Faithfulness

"His compassions fail not. They are new every morning" (Lamentations 3:22-23)

With confidence and reverence

1. "Great is Thy faith-ful-ness," O God my Fa-ther,
2. Sum-mer and win-ter, and spring-time and har-vest,
3. Par-don for sin and a peace that en-dur-eth,

There is no shad-ow of turn-ing with Thee;
Sun, moon and stars in their cours-es a-bove,
Thine own dear pres-ence to cheer and to guide;

Thou chang-est not, Thy com-pas-sions, they fail not;
Join with all na-ture in man-i-fold wit-ness
Strength for to-day and bright hope for to-mor-row,

As Thou hast been Thou for-ev-er wilt be.
To Thy great faith-ful-ness, mer-cy and love.
Bless-ings all mine, with ten thou-sand be-side!

CHORUS

"Great is Thy faith - ful - ness! Great is Thy faith - ful - ness!"

Morn - ing by morn - ing new mer - cies I see;

All I have need - ed Thy hand hath pro - vid - ed.

"Great is Thy faith - ful - ness," Lord, un - to me!

TEXT: Thomas O. Chisholm
MUSIC: FAITHFULNESS, by William M. Runyan

Stand Up, Stand Up for Jesus

"But the people that do know their God shall be strong, and do exploits" (Daniel 11:32)

Resolutely

1. Stand up, stand up for Je - sus, ye sol - diers of the cross;
2. Stand up, stand up for Je - sus, the trum - pet call o - bey;
3. Stand up, stand up for Je - sus; stand in His strength a - lone;
4. Stand up, stand up for Je - sus; the strife will not be long;

Lift high His roy - al ban - ner, it must not suf - fer loss:
Forth to the might - y con - flict in this His glo - rious day:
The arm of flesh will fail you; ye dare not trust your own:
This day, the noise of bat - tle, the next, the vic - tor's song:

From vic - tory un - to vic - tory His ar - my shall He lead,
Ye that are men, now serve Him a - gainst un - num - bered foes;
Put on the gos - pel ar - mor; each piece put on with prayer;
To him that o - ver - com - eth, a crown of life shall be;

Till ev - 'ry foe is van - quished, and Christ is Lord in - deed.
Let cour - age rise with dan - ger, and strength to strength op - pose.
Where du - ty calls, or dan - ger, be nev - er want - ing there.
He, with the King of glo - ry, shall reign e - ter - nal - ly!

TEXT: George Duffield
MUSIC: George James Webb

Come, Ye Thankful People, Come

"And ye shall eat in plenty, and be satisfied, and praise the name of the Lord your God" (Joel 2:26)

1. Come, ye thank-ful peo-ple, come, raise the song of har-vest home;
2. All the bless-ings of the field, all the stores the gar-dens yield;
3. These to Thee, our God, we owe, source whence all our bless-ings flow,

All is safe-ly gath-ered in ere the win-ter storms be-gin;
All the fruits in full sup-ply, rip-ened 'neath the sum-mer sky;
And for these our souls shall raise grate-ful songs of sol-emn praise.

God, our Mak-er, doth pro-vide for our wants to be sup-plied;
All that spring, with boun-teous hand, scat-ters o'er the smil-ing land;
Come, then, thank-ful peo-ple, come, raise the song of har-vest home;

Come to God's own tem-ple, come, raise the song of har-vest home.
All that lib-eral au-tumn pours, from her rich o'er-flow-ing stores.
Come to God's own tem-ple, come, raise the song of har-vest home.

TEXT: Henry Alford & Hugh Hartshorne
MUSIC: George J. Elvey

The Mountain of the Lord

"...shall be established in the top of the mountains" (Micah 4:1)

Eagerly

1. In the lat - ter days it shall come to pass
2. Out of Zi - on shall the law go forth,
3. They shall beat their swords in - to plow - shares,
4. Un - der - neath the vine and the fig tree,

That the moun - tain of the house of the Lord
From Je - ru - sa - lem the Word of the Lord.
In - to prun - ing hooks their spears shall be made.
Ev' - ry man shall sit in peace un - a - fraid,

Shall be lift - ed a - bove the oth - er na - tions,
He shall judge be - tween man - y peo - ples,
Na - tion shall not lift sword a - gainst na - tion,
For the mouth of the Lord of Hosts has spo - ken it,

And the na - tions will come and say,
And re - buke strong and dis - tant lands.
Nei - ther shall they learn war an - y more.
And for - ev - er we'll walk in His name.

CHORUS

"Come and let us go up to the moun-tain of the Lord,

To the house of Ja - cob's God.

He will teach us His ways, we will walk in His paths.

Let us go to the moun-tain of the Lord."

TEXT: Micah 4:1-5
MUSIC: Mark Graham

Not by Might, nor by Power

"...but by my Spirit" (Zechariah 4:6)

With reassurance

1. God's peo - ple are re - mind - ed to stir up the gift He gives;
2. The Com - fort - er, the Fa - ther gives in Je - sus' Ho - ly Name;
3. "My peace I leave with you, and with you I will al - ways be;

His Spir - it dwells in us; be - cause He lives, we al - so live.
Brings all things to re - mem - brance, but we all must fan the flame.
Don't let your heart be trou - bled; trust in God and trust in me."

CHORUS

"Not of fear, but of God's great - ness and His love and sound ac - cord;

Not by your own might or pow - er, by my Spir - it," says the Lord.

TEXT: Zechariah 4:6, John 14:19, 26, 27 & II Timothy 1:6-7
MUSIC: Ross Jutsum

God the Omnipotent

"He will proclaim peace to the nations" (Zechariah 9:10)

With adoration

1. God the Om-nip-o-tent! King, who or-dain-est
2. God the all mer-ci-ful! Earth hath for-sak-en
3. God the all righ-teous One! Man hath de-fied Thee;
4. So shall we ren-der Thee thank-ful de-vo-tion,

Great winds Thy clar-ions, the light-nings Thy sword;
Thy pre-cepts ho-ly, and slight-ed Thy word;
Yet to e-ter-ni-ty stand-eth Thy word;
For Thy de-liv-'rance from per-il and sword,

Show forth Thy pit-y on high where Thou reign-est,
Bid not Thy wrath in its ter-rors a-wak-en;
False-hood and wrong shall not tar-ry be-side Thee;
Sing-ing in cho-rus from o-cean to o-cean,

Give to us peace, O most mer-ci-ful Lord.
Give to us peace, O most mer-ci-ful Lord.
Pros-per the right, O most mer-ci-ful Lord.
"Thine is the pow'r and the glo-ry, O Lord."

TEXT: Henry F. Chorley & John Ellerton, based on Psalm 29
MUSIC: RUSSIAN HYMN, by Alexis Lwoff, 1833

Behold, the Day Will Come

"In that day shall there be one Lord, and His name one" (Zechariah 14:9)

Jubilantly

1. Be - hold, the day will come, the day of the Lord our God!
2. In that great day of God, our Lord shall stand on earth!
3. In that great day of God, t'will be nei-ther day nor night;
4. Be - hold, that day shall come, when all na-tions shall o - bey!

He shall bring all na-tions in that day a - gainst Je - ru - sa - lem.
On the Mount of Ol - ives He shall stand, and the mount shall cleave in two!
But at e - ven-time it shall be light; it shall be one day to God.
Those of all the na-tions that are left, to Je - ru - sa - lem shall go;

They shall take the cit - y and share the spoil, in the ver - y midst of them;
There shall be a val - ley of mam - moth size; by the val - ley you shall flee;
Out from Zi - on shall liv - ing wa - ters flow to the east and to the west;
They shall e - ven go there from year to year, and shall keep the Feast of Booths;

Then our God E - ter - nal shall go forth, and shall fight a - gainst our foes!
For our God E - ter - nal shall be King, and shall rule o - ver all the earth!
Then our God E - ter - nal shall be King; in that day shall there be one God!
There shall be one God, the E - ter - nal, Who is King o - ver all the earth!

TEXT: Zechariah 14
MUSIC: Dwight Armstrong

Hearts of the Fathers

"He will turn the hearts of the fathers to their children..." (Malachi 4:6)

With conviction

1. Re - mem - ber Mos - es' law take heed, all faith - ful ser - vants pray,
2. Now chil - dren are a bless - ing too, the fruit of His re - ward;
3. With heal - ing in His wings, the Sun of righ - teous-ness shall stand,

E - li - jah, I will send to you be - fore that dread - ful day.
In days of youth, let us re - joice, be grate - ful to the Lord.
All na - tions turn un - to His way un - less He strike the land.

CHORUS

And He will turn the hearts of the fa - thers to their chil - dren, to God's way.

He will turn the hearts of the chil - dren to their fa - thers in that day.

TEXT: Psalm 127:3 & Malachi 4:1-6
MUSIC: Ross Jutsum

Rejoice and Be Glad!

"...for great is your reward in heaven" (Matthew 5:12)

Exuberantly

1. Bless - ed are the poor in spir - it, for theirs is the King - dom of heav'n;
2. Bless - ed are the meek in spir - it, for they shall in - her - it the earth;
3. Bless - ed are the ones op - pressed for theirs is the King - dom of heav'n;
4. Bless - ed are the peace - ful ones, for they shall be chil - dren of God;

Bless - ed are the mer - ci - ful, for they shall be for - giv'n.
Bless - ed are the thirs - ty ones, for God shall quench their thirst.
Bless - ed are the ones who mourn, for God shall com - fort them.
Bless - ed are the pure of heart, for they shall see their God.

CHORUS

Re - joice and be ex - ceed - ing glad, for great is your re - ward;

Re - joice, al - ways be thank - ful for your bless - ings from the Lord.

TEXT: Matthew 5:3-9
MUSIC: Ross Jutsum

Salt of the Earth

"Ye are the salt of the earth" (Matthew 5:13)

TEXT: Matthew 5:13-16
MUSIC: Mark Graham

198

Let Your Light So Shine

"...that they may see your good works, and glorify your Father which is in heaven" (Matthew 5:16)

Brightly

1. You're the salt of the earth, pre-serv-ers of life;
2. You're the light of the world, high up on a hill,
3. In this age at the end, we dai-ly must pray

If the salt should lose its fla-vor,
And your cit-y's shin-ing night-ly.
For the strength and help re-quired.

It is fit to be cast and tram-pled by men;
Put your light on a stand, not un-der a bowl;
Let us quiet-ly pre-serve and shine ev-'ry day,

So be sure to pre-serve your sa-vor.
Fill your house with the glow shin-ing bright-ly.
Press-ing forth to the prize that's de-sired.

TEXT: Matthew 5:13-16 & Philippians 3:14
MUSIC: Ross Jutsum

Love Your Enemies

"...That ye may be the children of your Father which is in heaven" (Matthew 5:45)

Courageously

1. You have heard peo-ple say, "You shall love your neigh-bor
2. Your re-ward will be great if your foe is hun-gry,
3. As our Fa-ther in heav'n, we should seek per-fec-tion

And hate your en-e-my."
You give him bread to eat.
And live in har-mo-ny.

You have heard peo-ple say, "Give an eye for an eye,"
You will heap coals of fire and then God will re-ward
As the sons of our God, al-ways gra-cious and kind,

But now I want you to see:
For help-ing him on his feet.
As Christ would want us to be.

CHORUS

Love your en - e - mies; bless those who curse you;

Serve those who hate you and pray for them all.

That you may be sons of your Fa - ther in heav - en,

Fol - low Christ's ex - am - ple and heed His call.

TEXT: Proverbs 25:21, 22, Matthew 5:43-48 & Luke 6:35-36
MUSIC: Ross Jutsum

Thine Is the Glory

"For Thine is the kingdom, and the power, and the glory, for ever" (Matthew 6:13)

Confidently

1. Thine is the glo - ry, ris - en, con-quering Son;
2. Lo! Je - sus meets us, ris - en from the tomb;
3. No more we doubt Thee, glo - rious Prince of life!

End - less is the vic - tory, Thou o'er death hast won.
Lov - ing - ly He greets us, scat - ters fear and gloom.
Life is naught with - out Thee: aid us in our strife.

An - gels in bright rai - ment rolled the stone a - way,
Let His church with glad - ness hymns of tri - umph sing,
Make us more than con - querors, through Thy death - less love:

Kept the fold - ed grave - clothes where Thy bod - y lay.
For her Lord now liv - eth: death hath lost its sting.
Bring us safe through Jor - dan by your pow'r a - bove.

CHORUS

Thine is the glo - ry, ris - en, con-quering Son;

End less is the vic - tory, Thou o'er death hast won.

TEXT: Edmond L. Budry, transcribed by R. Birch Hoyle
MUSIC: From "Judas Maccabeus" by George Friedrich Handel

204

Seek You First the Kingdom of God

"...and all these things shall be added unto you" (Matthew 6:33)

Fervently

1. Seek you first the King-dom of God and all His righ-teous-ness.
2. Serve the Lord with per-fect heart and with a will-ing mind.
3. Seek the Lord while He may be found, and call while He is near.

All these things He'll add to you, and He will rich-ly bless.
Lis-ten now and do your part; seek Him and you shall find.
Turn to Him, for-sake your way, and He will sure-ly hear.

Ask, and it shall be giv-en; seek, and you shall find;
You, the Lord has cho-sen; do the Work; be strong;
For His thoughts are not our thoughts, nor His ways our ways.

Knock, and it shall be o-pened; our God is gra-cious and kind.
Build your house for His tem-ple; to God sal-va-tion be-longs.
God will mer-ci-f'lly par-don and bless us all of our days.

Seek you first the King-dom of God and all His righ-teous-ness.
Serve the Lord with per-fect heart and with a will-ing mind.
Seek the Lord while He may be found, and call while He is near.

All these things He'll add to you, and He will rich-ly bless.
Lis-ten now and do your part; seek Him and you shall find.
Turn to Him, for-sake your way, and He will sure-ly hear.

TEXT: I Chronicles 28, Isaiah 55 & Matthew 6:33, 7:7
MUSIC: Ross Jutsum

Consider the Lilies

"Consider the lilies of the field, how they grow" (Matthew 6:28)

With surety

1. Con - sid - er the lil - ies and how they grow,
2. And look at the ra - vens up in the air,
3. If God clothes the grass of the field this way,
4. So there - fore I say, "Take no anx - ious care,

For they nev - er toil or spin you know,
For they nev - er sow or gath - er there,
Which lives and which dies in a sin - gle day,
For what you shall eat and what you shall wear,

Yet Sol - o - mon in all his fin - er - y
Yet your Fa - ther feeds them from day to day.
If God feeds the birds of the heav - ens too,
But seek first God's King - dom and righ - teous - ness,

Was nev - er ar - rayed like one of these.
Are you not of far more worth than they?
Will He not do e - ven more for you?
And with all these things you shall be blest."

TEXT: Matthew 6:25-33
MUSIC: Mark Graham

The Solid Rock

"...and it fell not: for it was founded upon a rock" (Matthew 7:25)

With surety

1. My hope is built on noth-ing less than Je-sus' blood and right-eous-ness.
2. When dark-ness seems to hide His face, I rest on His un-chang-ing grace.
3. His oath, His cov-e-nant, His blood sup-port me in the whelm-ing flood.
4. When He shall come with trum-pet sound, Oh, may I then in Him be found;

I dare not trust in man's weak frame, but whol-ly lean on Je-sus' name.
In ev-'ry high and storm-y gale, my an-chor holds with-in the vale.
When all a-round my soul gives way, He then is all my Hope and Stay.
Dressed in His right-teous-ness a-lone, fault-less to stand be-fore the throne.

REFRAIN

On Christ, the sol-id Rock, I stand; all oth-er ground is

sink-ing sand. All oth-er ground is sink-ing sand.

TEXT: Edward Mote
MUSIC: William B. Bradbury

Onward, Christian Soldiers!

"I will build My church; and the gates of hell shall not prevail against it" (Matthew 16:18)

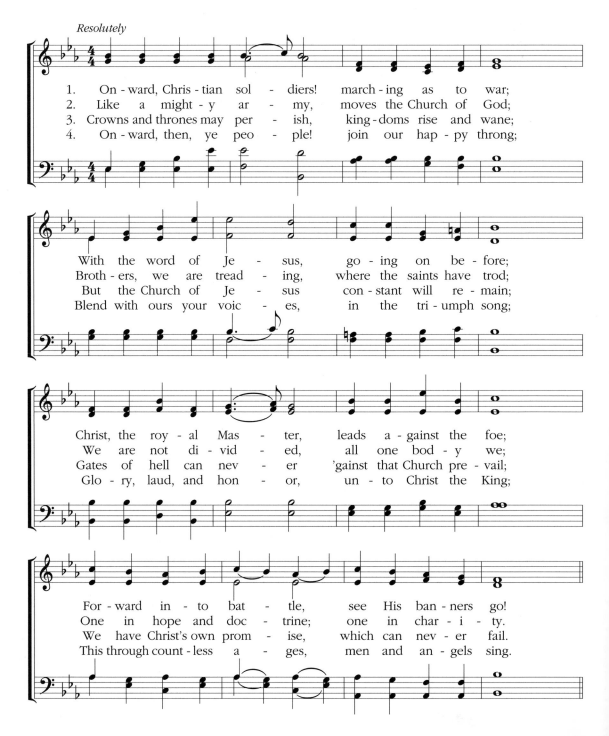

Resolutely

1. On - ward, Chris - tian sol - diers! march - ing as to war;
2. Like a might - y ar - my, moves the Church of God;
3. Crowns and thrones may per - ish, king - doms rise and wane;
4. On - ward, then, ye peo - ple! join our hap - py throng;

With the word of Je - sus, go - ing on be - fore;
Broth - ers, we are tread - ing, where the saints have trod;
But the Church of Je - sus con - stant will re - main;
Blend with ours your voic - es, in the tri - umph song;

Christ, the roy - al Mas - ter, leads a - gainst the foe;
We are not di - vid - ed, all one bod - y we;
Gates of hell can nev - er 'gainst that Church pre - vail;
Glo - ry, laud, and hon - or, un - to Christ the King;

For - ward in - to bat - tle, see His ban - ners go!
One in hope and doc - trine; one in char - i - ty.
We have Christ's own prom - ise, which can nev - er fail.
This through count - less a - ges, men and an - gels sing.

CHORUS

On - ward, Chris - tian sol - diers, march - ing as to war;

With the word of Je - sus, go - ing on be - fore.

TEXT: Sabine Baring-Gould
MUSIC: Arthur Sullivan

Forgive, and You Shall Be Forgiven

"...if he shall hear thee, thou hast gained thy brother" (Matthew 18:15)

With humility

1. How great is the love of our Fa-ther, Who calls us His dear sons!
2. When bring-ing your gift to the al-tar, you think of an of-fense;
3. To all our ex-am-ple of liv-ing should be a shin-ing light.

When Christ comes a-gain, we shall be like Him, we'll see Him as He is.
You go and be-come one with your broth - er, then bring your gift a-gain.
Be will-ing-ly un-der au-thor-i - ty, give due re-spect to all.

And this is the love He has shown us, that Christ laid down His life for all,
And should some-one sin a - gainst you, go see him, you and he a-lone;
And if you en-dure pain and suf-f'ring from un-just cause or o-ver-sight,

So we ought to lay down our lives for our broth-ers, to this end you are called.
Be kind, have com-pas-sion, let go of your an-ger and be at peace a-gain.
Then stand strong and live Christ's ex-am-ple be-fore us; trust Him Who judg-es all.

CHORUS

Forgive and you shall be forgiven;

Show mercy and this you will have too.

Do good to all, even your enemies.

Be merciful to others as your Father is to you.

TEXT: Matthew 5:23-24, Colossians 3:13-15, I Peter 2:12-23 & I John 3:1, 16
MUSIC: Ruth Myrick

This Child We Dedicate to Thee

"Let the little children come to me…for the kingdom of heaven belongs to such as these" (Matthew 19:14)

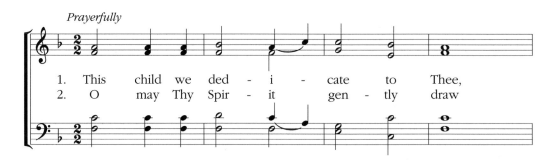

1. This child we ded - i - cate to Thee,
2. O may Thy Spir - it gen - tly draw

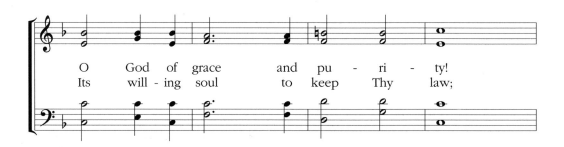

O God of grace and pu - ri - ty!
Its will - ing soul to keep Thy law;

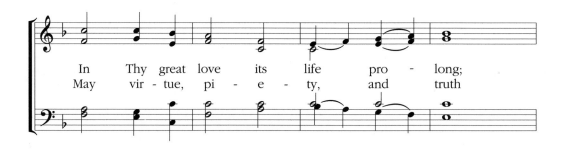

In Thy great love its life pro - long;
May vir - tue, pi - e - ty, and truth

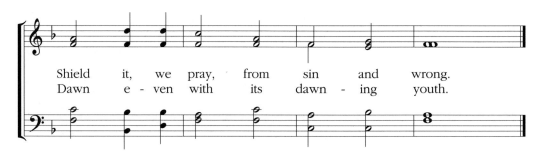

Shield it, we pray, from sin and wrong.
Dawn e - ven with its dawn - ing youth.

TEXT: From the German, transcribed by Samuel Gilman
MUSIC: FEDERAL STREET by Henry K. Oliver

Forgive as Christ Forgave

"I say not unto thee, Until seven times: but, Until seventy times seven" (Matthew 18:22)

Warm-heartedly

1. When Pe - ter came and said to Je - sus, "Lord, how oft should I for - give?"
2. If we con - fess to Christ our weak - ness, He is faith - ful to for - give;
3. If we for - give men their trans - gres - sions, God our Fa - ther us for - gives;

"Do not cease with on - ly sev - en, but as long as you shall live."
He will cleanse us from all e - vil and will teach us how to live.
And our sins He'll not re - mem - ber; then for - ev - er we shall live.

CHORUS

Be you kind and ten - der - heart - ed and for - give as Christ for - gave.

Through His blood we have re - demp - tion; by His grace we shall be saved.

TEXT: Matthew 6:12, Matthew 18, Ephesians 1:7, 2:5 & I John 1:9
MUSIC: Ross Jutsum

214

With God All Things Are Possible

"With men this is impossible; but with God all things are possible" (Matthew 19:26)

With unwavering confidence

1. Un - to the breth - ren Je - sus said, "At first you must be - lieve,
2. Christ raised the dead and healed the sick, turned wa - ter in - to wine.
3. When Christ sits on His glo - rious throne, and all the earth will sing,

And e - ven as a mus - tard seed, through faith you must re - ceive."
He fed the hun - gry mul - ti - tudes, gave sight un - to the blind.
Then those who've fol - lowed in His way shall reign as priests and kings.

CHORUS

And as we walk through life we find, with men it can't be done.

With God all things are pos - si - ble through Je - sus Christ His Son.

TEXT: Matthew 19:26 & Revelation 5:10
MUSIC: Ross Jutsum

All Glory, Laud and Honor

"Blessed is He that cometh in the name of the Lord" (Matthew 21:9)

With joy and dignity

1. All glo-ry, laud and hon - or to Thee, Re-deem-er, King,
2. The com-pa-ny of an - gels are prais-ing Thee on high,
3. To Thee, be-fore Thy pas - sion, they sang their hymns of praise;

To whom the lips of chil - dren make loud ho-san-nas ring!
And mor-tal men and all things cre-at-ed make re-ply.
To Thee, now high ex-alt - ed, our mel-o-dy we raise.

Thou art the King of Is - re'l, Thou Da-vid's roy-al Son,
The peo-ple of the He - brews with psalms be-fore Thee went;
Thou didst ac-cept their prais - es; ac-cept the praise we bring,

Who in the Lord's name com - est, the King and bless-ed One.
Our praise and prayer and an - thems be-fore Thee we pre-sent.
Who in all good de-light - est, Thou good and gra-cious King.

TEXT: Theodulph of Orleans, c. 820; translated by J. M. Neale, 1854
MUSIC: Melchior Teschner, 1615

Inherit the Kingdom

"...prepared for you since the creation of the world" (Matthew 25:34)

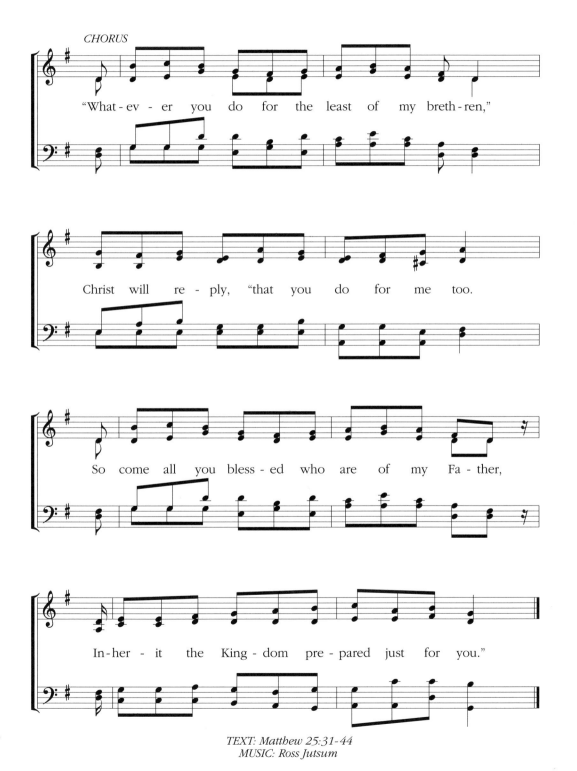

CHORUS

"What-ev-er you do for the least of my breth-ren," Christ will re-ply, "that you do for me too. So come all you bless-ed who are of my Fa-ther, In-her-it the King-dom pre-pared just for you."

TEXT: Matthew 25:31-44
MUSIC: Ross Jutsum

Lo, He Comes With Clouds Descending

"...they shall see the Son of Man coming in the clouds of heaven" (Matthew 24:30)

With great anticipation

1. Lo, He comes with clouds de-scend-ing, once for fa-vored sin-ners slain;
2. Now re-demp-tion, long ex-pect-ed, see in sol-emn pomp ap-pear:
3. Yea, A-men! Let all a-dore Thee, high on Thine e-ter-nal throne;

Thou-sand thou-sand saints at-tend-ing, swell the tri-umph of His train:
All His saints, by men re-ject-ed, now shall meet Him in the air:
Sav-ior, take the pow'r and glo-ry; claim the King-dom for Thine own:

Al-le-lu-ia! Al-le-lu-ia! God ap-pears on earth to reign.
Al-le-lu-ia! Al-le-lu-ia! See the day of God ap-pear.
O, come quick-ly, O, come quick-ly! Ev-er-last-ing God, come down.

TEXT: Charles Wesley and Martin Madan; based on John Cennick
MUSIC: Henry T. Smart

O Sacred Head, Now Wounded

"When they had platted a crown of thorns, they put it upon His head" (Matthew 27:29)

With solemnity

1. O sa-cred Head, now wound-ed, with grief and shame weighed down,
2. What Thou, my Lord, hast suf-fered was all for sin-ners' gain;
3. What lan-guage shall I bor-row to thank Thee, dear-est friend,

Now scorn-ful-ly sur-round-ed with thorns, Thy on-ly crown,
Mine, mine was the trans-gres-sion, but Thine the dead-ly pain.
For this Thy dy-ing sor-row, Thy pit-y with-out end?

How art Thou pale with an-guish, with sore a-buse and scorn!
Lo, here I fall, my Sav-ior! 'Tis I de-serve Thy place;
O make me Thine for-ev-er; And, should I faint-ing be,

How does that vis-age lan-guish which once was bright as morn!
Look on me with Thy fa-vor, vouch-safe to me Thy grace.
Lord, let me nev-er, nev-er out-live my love for Thee!

TEXT: Latin, 12th century; German, Paul Gerhardt; transcribed by James W. Alexander
MUSIC: From "Passion Chorale" by Hans Leo Hassler; harmonized by J. S. Bach

Go Ye Therefore Into All the World

"...teaching them to observe all things whatsoever I have commanded you" (Matthew 28:20)

Confidently; in moderate tempo

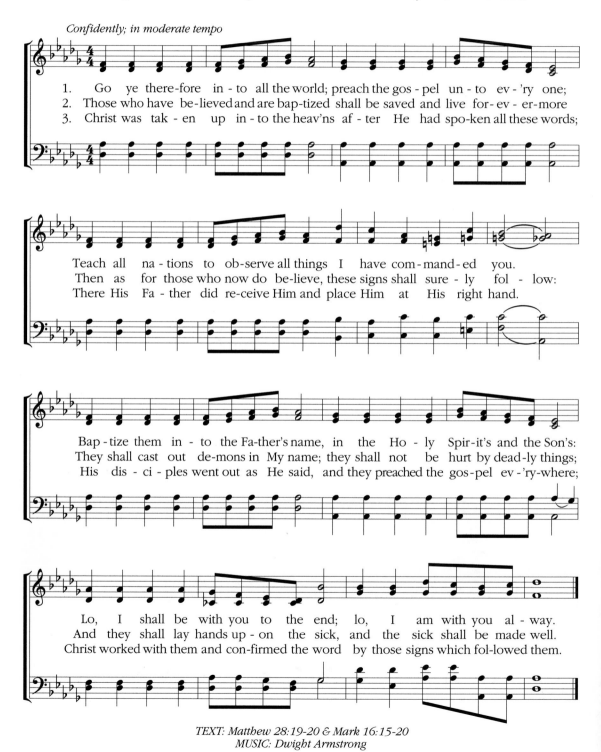

1. Go ye there-fore in-to all the world; preach the gos-pel un-to ev-'ry one;
2. Those who have be-lieved and are bap-tized shall be saved and live for-ev-er-more
3. Christ was tak-en up in-to the heav'ns af-ter He had spo-ken all these words;

Teach all na-tions to ob-serve all things I have com-mand-ed you.
Then as for those who now do be-lieve, these signs shall sure-ly fol-low:
There His Fa-ther did re-ceive Him and place Him at His right hand.

Bap-tize them in-to the Fa-ther's name, in the Ho-ly Spir-it's and the Son's;
They shall cast out de-mons in My name; they shall not be hurt by dead-ly things;
His dis-ci-ples went out as He said, and they preached the gos-pel ev-'ry-where;

Lo, I shall be with you to the end; lo, I am with you al-way.
And they shall lay hands up-on the sick, and the sick shall be made well.
Christ worked with them and con-firmed the word by those signs which fol-lowed them.

TEXT: Matthew 28:19-20 & Mark 16:15-20
MUSIC: Dwight Armstrong

Go and Teach All Nations

"I am with you always, to the very end of the age" (Matthew 28:20)

With conviction

1. "Go and teach all na-tions, bap-tiz-ing in the name
2. "God has giv'n all pow-er in heav'n and earth to me.
3. When our Lord de-part-ed, to God He did as-cend.

Of Fa-ther, Son, and Ho-ly Spir-it, and my words pro-claim.
You shall re-ceive my pow'r and truth and they shall make you free.
Dis-ci-ples in Je-ru-sa-lem sang prais-es to the heav'ns;

My Fa-ther tells His chil-dren that the Lord, He will de-fend;
Re-pen-tance and for-give-ness shall be preached in ev-'ry land,
And Christ is with us al-ways, and His mes-sage is the same.

For I am with you al-ways, e-ven to the ver-y end."
And teach-ing of my way ob-serv-ing all that I com-mand."
So go and teach all na-tions and His pre-cious truth pro-claim.

TEXT: Zechariah 12:8, Matthew 28:18-20 & Luke 24:47-53
MUSIC: R'oss Jutsum

God So Loved the World

"...that He gave His only begotten Son" (John 3:16)

With great appreciation and joy

1. No one has seen or heard what our God de-sires of us;
2. So let us love all men, as the chil-dren God has called;
3. The love we show for God is the love we show to all;

A life of hope and joy, that will for-ev-er last.
So we may live in peace, with love that fills us all.
So how can we love God, if we don't hear His call?

CHORUS

For God so loved the world, that He gave His on-ly Son;

That all who trust in Him, shall e-ter-nal-ly live as one.

TEXT: John 3:16, I Corinthians 2:9 & I John 4:7
MUSIC: Ross Jutsum

I Am Thine, O Lord

"And I, if I be lifted up from the earth, will draw all men unto me" (John 12:32)

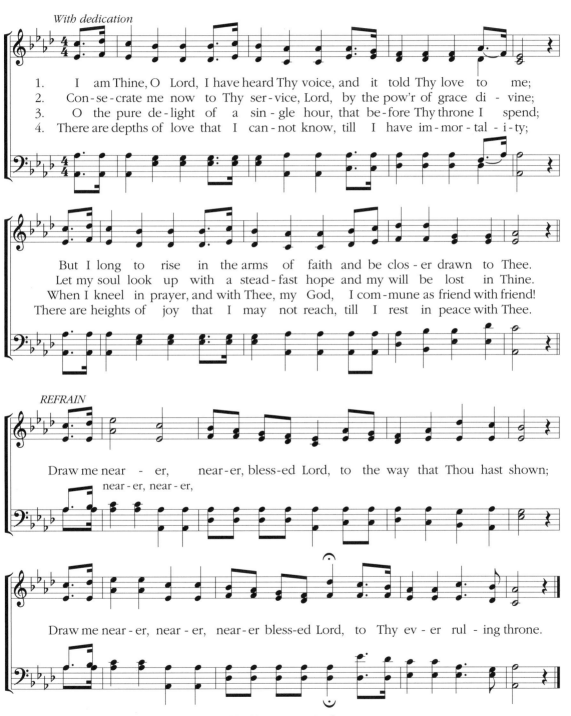

With dedication

1. I am Thine, O Lord, I have heard Thy voice, and it told Thy love to me;
2. Con-se-crate me now to Thy ser-vice, Lord, by the pow'r of grace di - vine;
3. O the pure de-light of a sin-gle hour, that be-fore Thy throne I spend;
4. There are depths of love that I can-not know, till I have im-mor-tal-i-ty;

But I long to rise in the arms of faith and be clos-er drawn to Thee.
Let my soul look up with a stead-fast hope and my will be lost in Thine.
When I kneel in prayer, and with Thee, my God, I com-mune as friend with friend!
There are heights of joy that I may not reach, till I rest in peace with Thee.

REFRAIN

Draw me near - er, near-er, bless-ed Lord, to the way that Thou hast shown;
near - er, near - er,

Draw me near - er, near - er, near-er bless-ed Lord, to Thy ev - er rul - ing throne.

TEXT: Fanny J. Crosby
MUSIC: W. H. Doann

If You Know These Things

"...happy are ye if ye do them" (John 13:17)

Reflectively; with expression

1. Just be-fore we take the bread and wine, there are les - sons to be learned;
2. When we see the dirt up - on our feet, and our sin, right from the start,
3. As our feet sup - port us ev - 'ry day to wher-ev - er we may go,

And our feet, the bod - y's low - est parts, help us hum - bly to dis - cern.
Then we re - al - ize we need His blood for a wash - ing of our hearts.
Hum - bly serve the man - y mem - bers of His bod - y here be - low.

When we look to all our breth - ren and es-teem them, free from pride;
Though our sins are just like scar - let, they shall be as white as snow;
Help them car - ry all their bur - dens and their pur - pose to ful - fill;

When we let His mind be in us, He will be our strength and guide.
When we fol - low His ex - am - ple, more like Him we're sure to grow.
For our Sav - ior came to serve us and to do our Fa - ther's will.

rit.

CHORUS

"If you call me Lord and Mas - ter, un - der-stand just what I do;

You should al - so wash each oth - er's feet, as I have done for you.

I have giv - en this ex - am - ple and will put you to the test;

If you know these things and do them, you sure - ly will be blessed."

TEXT: Isaiah 1:18 & John 13:1-17
MUSIC: Ross Jutsum

By This Shall All Men Know

"...that ye are my disciples, if ye have love one to another" (John 13:35)

With sincerity

1. A new com-mand-ment I will give, to mag-ni-fy the way to live:
2. Not called to be luke-warm or cold, but zeal-ous like the men of old;
3. I give my life for all man-kind, and call you at this spe-cial time;

Love each oth-er as you do, with the love I've giv-en you.
Do the will of God a-bove; grow in His e-ter-nal love.
Do the work and feed the flock; build your house up-on the Rock.

CHORUS

And by this shall all men know, all a-round the world you'll show,

That you are my dis-ci-ples, you're my sis-ter and my broth-er;

And by this shall all men know, ev - 'ry friend and ev - 'ry foe,

That you are my dis - ci - ples if you love one an - oth - er.

TEXT: John 13:34-35
MUSIC: Ross Jutsum

The Truth Shall Make You Free

"I am the way, the truth, and the life" (John 14:6)

Confidently; in graceful rhythm

1. "I'm the way   and the truth   and the life," He has said;
2. Je - sus said   that His King - dom is   not   of this world;

"No one comes   to the Fa - ther but by me."
He's the King;   for this rea - son He was born.

Let us love   not in word, but in deed   and in truth,
Ev - 'ry one   who re - joic - es in truth   hears His voice;

For His King - dom He'll give   us   the key.
They will reign   when His King - dom   shall dawn.

CHORUS

And His word is truth for e-ter-ni-ty;

He who speaks the truth in his heart will see.

So con-tin - ue His word; you're dis-ci - ples in-deed;

And you shall know His truth, and the truth

Shall make you free.

TEXT: Matthew 16:19, John 8:32, 14:6, 18:37 & I John 3:18
MUSIC: Ross Jutsum

God Speaks to Us

"Let not your heart be troubled: ye believe in God, believe also in me" (John 14:1)

With anticipation

Trumpets before each stanza

1. God speaks to us; by His great pow'r we're led;
2. In God's vast realm are man-y of-fic-es;
3. And when this place has been pre-pared for you,

Let not your hearts be-come dis-qui-et-ed.
Were it not so, I sure-ly would have said;
I will re-turn; with me you shall be, too;

You trust in God; be-lieve and trust in me;
For I must go, a place for you pre-pare;
So that where I am you may al-so be;

You trust in God; be-lieve and trust in me.
For I must go, a place for you pre-pare.
So that where I am you may al-so be.

TEXT: John 14:1-3
MUSIC: George W. Warren

Greater Love

"...hath no man than this, that a man lay down his life for his friends" (John 15:13)

With tender feeling

1. This is my com-mand that you love each oth - er   as   I   have loved you all.
2. Love the Lord E - ter - nal with all your be - ing,   with heart and soul and mind.
3. Pray for all your foes, bless all those who curse you,   and love   your en - e - mies.

This is   my com-mand that you love each oth - er,   be sure   to heed my   call.
Al - ways love your neigh-bor as he would love you,   show love   to all man - kind.
Pray and al-ways help those who hate and use you,   and God   will be well pleased.

CHORUS

Great - er   love has no one than this, than to lay down his life for his friends;

You're my friends if you do what I say, and I'll guide and pro-tect till the end.

TEXT: Matthew 5:44, Luke 10:27, John 15:12-14 & Hebrews 13:5
MUSIC: Ross Jutsum

232

We Praise Thee, O God, Our Redeemer

"Being justified...through the redemption that is in Christ Jesus" (Romans 3:24)

With thanksgiving

1. We praise Thee, O God, our Re-deem-er, Cre-at-or;
2. We wor-ship Thee, God of our fa-thers, we bless Thee;
3. With voic-es u-nit-ed our prais-es we of-fer;

In grate-ful de-vo-tion our trib-ute we bring.
Through life's storm and tem-pest our Guide hast Thou been.
To Thee, great E-ter-nal, glad an-thems we raise.

We lay it be-fore Thee; we kneel and a-dore Thee;
When per-ils o'er-take us, es-cape Thou wilt make us,
Thy strong arm will guide us; our God is be-side us;

We bless Thy ho-ly name: glad prais-es we sing.
And with Thy help, O Lord, our bat-tles we win.
To Thee, our great Re-deem-er, for-ev-er be praise.

TEXT: Julis Bulk Cady
MUSIC: Netherlands Folk Song

The Gift of Life

"...the gift of God is eternal life through Jesus Christ our Lord" (Romans 6:23)

With deep gratitude

1. The gift of life from God a-bove, is life He cre-at-ed with love;
2. The gift of life from God di-vine, is life He cre-at-ed for man;
3. The gift of life from God Who lives, is life that He free-ly gives;

He made all things and by His might-y hand, life rings through-out the land.
He is our God and we His peo-ple are, ev-'ry-where near and far.
He of-fers us the great-est gift of all, life for e-ter-ni-ty.

CHORUS

With all my heart I will sing to God, with all my heart I'll give praise;

With all my heart, I'll sing un-to God, with all of my heart give thanks.

TEXT: Romans 5:18, 6:23 & II Corinthians 9:15
MUSIC: Sarah S. Bilowus

All Things Work Together

"...for good to them that love God" (Romans 8:28)

With confidence

1. Jo - seph, son of Is - r'el, was by his broth - ers sold;
2. Je - sus' own dis - ci - ple be - trayed his Mas - ter's love;
3. In this life there's sor - row and all too of - ten pain,
4. Jo - seph, we re - mem - ber, was E - gypt's great - est one;

Caused by jeal - ous en - vy of what his dreams fore - told.
Thir - ty coins of sil - ver did buy Mes - si - ah's blood.
But these things shall fade a - way as we be - gin to reign.
Je - sus, first - born Son of God, is by His Fa - ther's throne.

Then, far from home in ser - vi - tude and in - to pris - on's dread,
A night and day of tor - ment, a death too hard to know;
One hun - dred - fold He gives us for things we give for Him;
Now, none of life's dis - plea - sures should ev - er be com - pared

Through it all young Jo - seph was by his Cre - a - tor led.
Seemed as though all hope was gone un - til the stone was rolled.
His great joy and fam - i - ly and life that nev - er ends.
To the end - less glo - ry God has for us to share.

CHORUS

All things work to - geth - er, all things work for good;

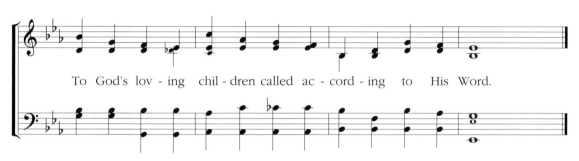

To God's lov - ing chil - dren called ac - cord - ing to His Word.

TEXT: Thomas Hammett
MUSIC: Thomas Hammett

God's Everlasting Love

"...nor anything else in all creation, will be able to separate us from the love of God" (Romans 8:39)

With unshakable confidence

1. God did not spare His on-ly Son, but gave Him up for ev-'ry-one,
2. If God be for us, who can stand? He gives to us His guid-ing hand.
3. Shall trib-u-la-tion or dis-tress di-vide us from His ho-li-ness?

To be our Sav-ior and our King; He free-ly gives us ev-'ry-thing.
We're more than con-querors by His will; for-ev-er He will love us still.
Nor per-se-cu-tion or the sword shall keep us from our lov-ing Lord.

CHORUS

Not things to come, nor life nor death, no an-gels, pow-ers, height nor depth;

For I'm per-suad-ed by God a-bove that none can change His last-ing love.

TEXT: John 3:16 & Romans 8:31-39
MUSIC: Ross Jutsum

Not Many Wise Men Now Are Called

"God hath chosen the foolish things of the world to confound the wise" (I Corinthians 1:27)

In stately rhythm

1. Not man-y wise men now are called, not man-y no-ble breth-ren,
2. God chose the fool-ish of the world; He chose the weak and base things;
3. E-ven the fool-ish-ness of God, wis-er by far than man is;

Not man-y might-y cho-sen ones, for you see your call-ing:
He chose the things which are de-spised, that no flesh should glo-ry.
E-ven the weak-ness of our God, strong-er far than man is.

Sons of God, you are called, not be-cause of great-ness;
Sons of God, you are called, not be-cause of great-ness;
Sons of God, you are called, not be-cause of great-ness;

E-ven the wis-dom of man-kind is to God but fool-ish.
You who are called and now in Christ shall con-found the might-y.
Let them who glo-ry boast in Christ, not in their own great-ness.

TEXT: I Corinthians 1:25-31
MUSIC: Dwight Armstrong

Let Us Keep the Feast

"...with the unleavened bread of sincerity and truth" (I Corinthians 5:8)

1. On the fif-teenth day of the first month is the Feast of Un-leav-ened Bread;
2. Bread of Life, God free-ly has giv-en: Liv-ing Bread for us to re-ceive;

All our bread is com-plete-ly un-leav-ened sev-en days, as our Fa-ther has said:
When we come to our Lord we'll not hun-ger, nor will thirst if we tru-ly be-lieve.

The first and last shall be Ho-ly Days, to help us walk in His way;
When Christ re-turns to bring peace on earth and all the world will be free,

We'll bring an of-f'ring un-to the Lord, re-joic-ing with Him each day.
He'll fill the earth with God's knowl-edge as the wa-ters cov-er the sea.

CHORUS *a tempo*

There-fore let us keep the Feast, not with the old bread of un-righ-teous-ness;

Let us keep the Feast, nei-ther with leav-en of mal-ice and wick-ed-ness.

Let's en-joy the Feast, ev-'ry a-dult and child and youth:

The Feast of Un-leav-ened Bread, bread of sin-cer-i-ty and truth.

TEXT: Leviticus 23:6-8, Isaiah 11:9, John 6:33-35 & I Corinthians 5:8
MUSIC: Ross Jutsum

Christ, Our Passover

"This do in remembrance of me" (I Corinthians 11:24)

With deep devotion

1. Je - sus knew that the time to de - part had now ar - rived;
2. And while we were still sin - ners, Christ died for all our sins,
3. Let us fo - cus our eyes on our Sav - ior and our King,
4. He will nev - er for - sake us, He'll nev - er leave His sons

He must go to the Fa - ther up a - bove.
Gave His life as a sac - ri - fice for all;
As per - fect - er and au - thor of our faith.
And His daugh - ters will nev - er be a - lone.

Hav - ing loved His dis - ci - ples un - to the ver - y end,
Show - ing love and com - pas - sion for all His fam - i - ly,
For the joy set be - fore Him, our Lord en - dured the cross
In - ter - ced - ing for sis - ters and broth - ers that He loves;

Now He showed them the full - ness of His love.
Je - sus Christ, He has rec - on - ciled us all.
So that we all would run and win the race.
Serv - ing all of God's chil - dren from His throne.

CHORUS

"This bread is my bod-y bro-ken for you; do this in re-mem-brance of me.

This cup, the new cov-e-nant is my blood, by which you shall all be re-deemed.

Now Christ is our Pass-o-ver sac-ri-ficed; e-ter-nal life showed us the way.

We'll take up our cross and de-ny our-selves as we faith-ful-ly fol-low each day.

TEXT: Luke 9:23, Romans 5:8, I Corinthians 9:24, 11:24-26, Hebrews 7:25, 12:1-2 & 13:5
MUSIC: Ross Jutsum

If I Have Not Charity

"I am become as sounding brass, or a tinkling cymbal" (I Corinthians 13:1)

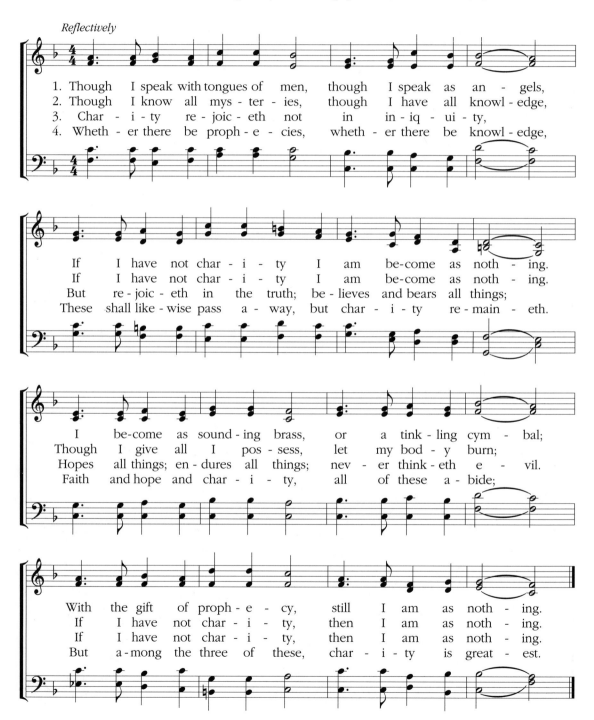

Reflectively

1. Though I speak with tongues of men, though I speak as an - gels,
2. Though I know all mys - ter - ies, though I have all knowl - edge,
3. Char - i - ty re - joic - eth not in in - iq - ui - ty,
4. Wheth - er there be proph - e - cies, wheth - er there be knowl - edge,

If I have not char - i - ty I am be - come as noth - ing.
If I have not char - i - ty I am be - come as noth - ing.
But re - joic - eth in the truth; be - lieves and bears all things;
These shall like - wise pass a - way, but char - i - ty re - main - eth.

I be - come as sound - ing brass, or a tink - ling cym - bal;
Though I give all I pos - sess, let my bod - y burn;
Hopes all things; en - dures all things; nev - er think - eth e - vil.
Faith and hope and char - i - ty, all of these a - bide;

With the gift of proph - e - cy, still I am as noth - ing.
If I have not char - i - ty, then I am as noth - ing.
If I have not char - i - ty, then I am as noth - ing.
But a - mong the three of these, char - i - ty is great - est.

TEXT: I Corinthians 13
MUSIC: Dwight Armstrong

Love Never Fails

"These three remain: faith, hope and love. But the greatest of these is love" (I Corinthians 13:13)

With devotion

1. And though I speak with tongues of men and yet I have not love,
2. And though I have the gift to teach and un-der - stand all things;
3. And though I give to feed the poor, but love I have not found;

And though I am as sound-ing brass, a sound not heard a - bove,
And with great faith, the moun-tains move, yet lit - tle joy it brings.
And give my bod - y to be burned, yet still my hands are bound.

CHORUS

Love nev - er fails or seeks its own, a trea-sure for your youth.

Love suf-fers long and love is kind, re - joic - es in the truth.

TEXT: I Corinthians 13:1-13
MUSIC: Caroline Sag & Ross Jutsum

The Trumpet Shall Sound

"Thanks be to God, which giveth us the victory through our Lord Jesus Christ" (I Corinthians 15:57)

Triumphantly

1. Be - hold, I show, I show you all a mys - te - ry:
2. O death, O grave, where is your sting, your vic - to - ry?

We shall not sleep, but we shall all be changed.
The sting of death is sin, de - fined by law.

In just a while, the twin - kling of an eye, you'll see,
And when this mor - tal puts on im - mor - tal - i - ty,

The trum - pet shall sound, and we shall all be raised.
The trum - pet shall sound; re - joice for - ev - er - more.

CHORUS

But thanks to God, Who giv - eth us the vic - to - ry

Through Christ the Lord, E - ter - nal, Liv - ing One.

Al - ways a - bound and do the work He's giv - en me,

Be - lov - ed of God and Christ, His cho - sen sons.

TEXT: I Corinthians 15:50-58
MUSIC: Ross Jutsum

Ambassadors for Christ

"...Be reconciled to God" (II Corinthians 5:20)

With courage and conviction

1. If an-y-one is in Christ, then he is a new cre-a-tion;
2. As fel-low work-ers with Him, it's the day of our sal-va-tion;
3. God said He's dwell-ing with us, and He's walk-ing with His peo-ple;

The old has passed a-way and all things are made new.
So let us not re-ceive the grace of God in vain.
He prom-ised He would guide and lead the path we trod.

The min-is-try of our Christ, one of rec-on-cil-i-a-tion,
With pu-ri-ty and with love, let us serve our Lord and Mas-ter;
And now He's dwell-ing in us, and we are His sons and daugh-ters;

Mak-ing peace with God the Fa-ther and with all our breth-ren too.
As we press to-ward His King-dom, let us nev-er be a-shamed.
For we are the ho-ly tem-ple of the ev-er-liv-ing God.

CHORUS

We are there-fore Christ's am-bas-sa-dors and called to be God's sons,

To de-clare His ho-ly King-dom, that His will on earth be done.

Be rec-on-ciled to God and let us com-mit our hearts and minds;

Am-bas-sa-dors for Je-sus Christ, the Sav-ior of all man-kind.

TEXT: Matthew 6:10, II Corinthians 5:17-21, 6:1-2, 6, 16-18 & Philippians 3:14
MUSIC: Ross Jutsum

God Loves a Cheerful Giver

"He which soweth bountifully shall reap also bountifully" (II Corinthians 9:6)

Lively; with dedication

1. Who-so-ev-er sow-eth spar-ing-ly shall reap just like he sows;
2. He has scat-tered and dis-persed a-broad His gifts un-to the poor;
3. Three times in a year you shall ap-pear to hear of Christ's good news;
4. When you give an of-f'ring to the Lord, don't give re-luc-tant-ly,

And who-ev-er sows a-bun-dant-ly reaps more than he can know.
He has mul-ti-plied the seed you've sown; His righ-teous-ness en-dures.
Come be-fore the Lord your God un-to the place that He shall choose.
Nor be-cause you feel o-bliged to give, but of-fer cheer-ful-ly.

God can make all grace a-bound to you, al-ways in ev-'ry-thing;
All the ser-vice you per-form sup-plies the needs of His own sons,
On each Ho-ly Day as-sem-bly, sing to Him with one ac-cord;
An-nual Ho-ly Days re-mind us all of His great mas-ter plan,

Man-y bless-ings flow, when we, to Him, our free-will of-f'rings bring.
O-ver-flow-ing with ex-pres-sions of the thanks from cho-sen ones.
Ev-'ry man shall give ac-cord-ing to his bless-ings from the Lord.
And our free-will of-f'rings show our love to God and fel-low-man.

CHORUS

God loves a cheer-ful giv - er, who gives right from the heart;

He prom-is - es to de - liv - er; His bless-ings He'll im - part.

TEXT: Deuteronomy 16:16 & II Corinthians 9:6-14
MUSIC: Ross Jutsum

Crucified With Christ

"...and I no longer live, but Christ lives in me" (Galatians 2:20)

With humility and conviction

1. Sal - va - tion found in no one else, with Him we shall be raised;
2. If we, con - fess - ing Christ is Lord, with all our hearts be - lieve
3. God raised Him from the dead, this Je - sus Christ we cru - ci - fied
4. This prom - ise is for us and for our chil - dren, one and all:

No oth - er name is giv'n to men by which we must be saved.
That God has raised Him from the dead, His Spir - it, we re - ceive.
And made our Je - sus Lord and Christ; for all our sins He died.
For those who live far off, for all the Lord our God will call.

The res - ur - rec - tion and the life, the Son of God Most High;
We can - not say that Christ is Lord ex - cept His Spir - it guides;
Re - pent and be bap - tized and seek for - give - ness in His name;
And who re - ceives His chil - dren should re - ceive them in His name.

Be - lieve Him, live for - ev - er, e - ven though we sure - ly die.
We're raised with Him and our lives with Christ in God we hide.
Re - ceive the Ho - ly Spir - it, God's great gift for us to claim.
So wel - come Christ our Sav - ior and the One from whence He came.

CHORUS

I am cru-ci-fied with Christ, and I no long-er live;

I live by faith in God's own Son, Whose life for me did give.

It's a new birth to a liv-ing hope; God has raised Him from the dead.

And with God's gift, Christ with-in me, by His Spir-it I am lead.

TEXT: John 11:25, Acts 2:36-39, 4:12, Romans 10:9, I Cor. 7:14, 12:3, II Cor. 4:14, Col. 3:3 & I Peter 1:3
MUSIC: Ross Jutsum

The Fruit of the Spirit

"...against such there is no law" (Galatians 5:23)

With conviction

1. "I am the vine, you are the branch-es, you who a-bide in me.
2. If we live in the Spir-it, let us walk and grow;

For with-out me, you can do noth-ing; in you I'll al-ways be."
Ev-'ry tree brings forth fruit; by this you shall be known.

CHORUS

The fruit of the Spir-it is joy, pa-tience, peace and love,

Gen-tle-ness, good-ness, kind-ness and faith from our Fa-ther a-bove.

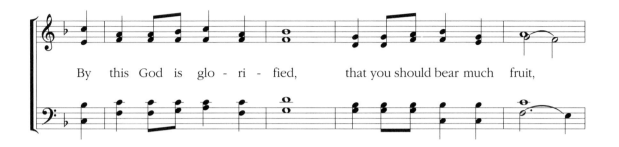

By this God is glo - ri - fied, that you should bear much fruit,

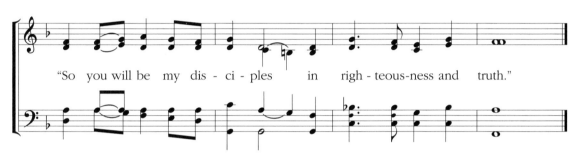

"So you will be my dis - ci - ples in righ - teous-ness and truth."

TEXT: Matthew 7:16, John 15:5-8, Galatians 5:22-23 & Ephesians 5:9
MUSIC: Ross Jutsum

The Church's One Foundation

"Christ also loved the church, and gave Himself for it" (Ephesians 5:25)

Expressively; with meditation

1. The Church-'s one foun - da - tion is Je - sus Christ her Lord;
2. E - lect from ev - 'ry na - tion, yet one o'er all the earth,
3. 'Mid toil and trib - u - la - tion, and tu - mults of her war,

She is His new cre - a - tion by wa - ter and the Word:
Her char - ter of sal - va - tion, one Lord, one faith, one birth;
She waits the con - sum - ma - tion of peace for - ev - er - more;

From heav'n He came and sought her to be His ho - ly bride;
His saints their watch are keep - ing; their cry goes up, "How long?"
Till with the vi - sion glo - rious her long - ing eyes are blest,

With His own blood He bought her, and for her life He died.
And soon the night of weep - ing shall be the morn of song.
And God's true Church vic - to - rious shall be the Church at rest.

TEXT: Samuel J. Stone, 1866
MUSIC: AURELIA by Samuel S. Wesley, 1864

Be Strong in the Lord

"Put on the whole armour of God" (Ephesians 6:11)

In stately rhythm

1. Be strong in the Lord your God, and with His whole ar - mor stand;
2. Ex - am - ine your ev - 'ry deed, and pray for His help right now;
3. God's ar - my is on the move, the sword of the Spir - it proves;

We wres - tle a - gainst the e - vil pow'rs of dark - ness and strife through - out the land.
Our Mas - ter pro - vides our ev - 'ry need; one day at His name all knees shall bow.
U - nit - ed in love and har - mo - ny, to - geth - er as one great fam - i - ly;

Keep wear - ing the belt of truth, the breast - plate of righ - teous - ness,
Ex - hort, com - fort, ed - i - fy; take heed of the words you've heard:
Ad - vanc - ing on ev - 'ry side with Christ as our King and guide;

The gos - pel of peace, the shield of faith; we will quench all the wick - ed - ness.
The hel - met of life, the shield of faith, and re - ly on your sword, God's Word.
His truth makes His cho - sen peo - ple free; He will lead us to vic - to - ry.

TEXT: I Corinthians 14:3, Ephesians 6:11-17 & Philippians 2:10
MUSIC: Ross Jutsum

One Faith, One Love

"...in one spirit, with one mind striving together for the faith" (Philippians 1:27)

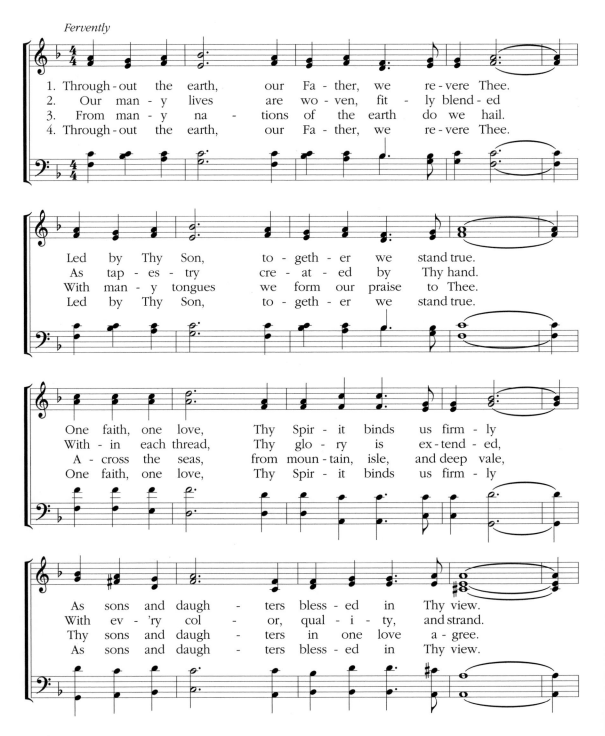

Fervently

1. Through-out the earth, our Fa-ther, we re-vere Thee.
2. Our man-y lives are wo-ven, fit-ly blend-ed
3. From man-y na-tions of the earth do we hail.
4. Through-out the earth, our Fa-ther, we re-vere Thee.

Led by Thy Son, to-geth-er we stand true.
As tap-es-try cre-at-ed by Thy hand.
With man-y tongues we form our praise to Thee.
Led by Thy Son, to-geth-er we stand true.

One faith, one love, Thy Spir-it binds us firm-ly
With-in each thread, Thy glo-ry is ex-tend-ed,
A-cross the seas, from moun-tain, isle, and deep vale,
One faith, one love, Thy Spir-it binds us firm-ly

As sons and daugh-ters bless-ed in Thy view.
With ev-'ry col-or, qual-i-ty, and strand.
Thy sons and daugh-ters in one love a-gree.
As sons and daugh-ters bless-ed in Thy view.

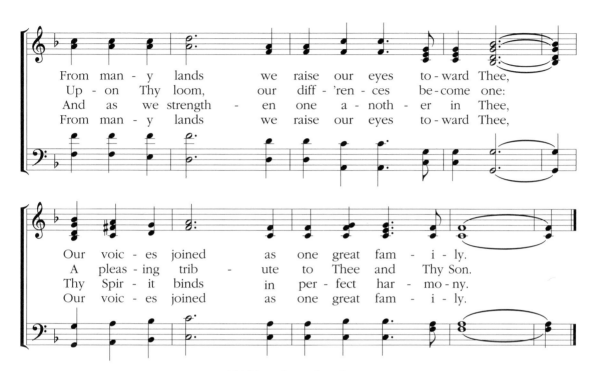

From man - y lands we raise our eyes to - ward Thee,
Up - on Thy loom, our diff - 'ren - ces be - come one:
And as we strength - en one a - noth - er in Thee,
From man - y lands we raise our eyes to - ward Thee,

Our voic - es joined as one great fam - i - ly.
A pleas - ing trib - ute to Thee and Thy Son.
Thy Spir - it binds in per - fect har - mo - ny.
Our voic - es joined as one great fam - i - ly.

TEXT: Paula Marler Johnson
MUSIC: FINLANDIA by Jean Sibelius, 1899

Let This Mind Be in You

"...which was also in Christ Jesus" (Philippians 2:5)

Humbly

1. Ful - fill His joy, my breth - ren, with like and low - ly minds;
2. Look not up - on your own things, but look to oth - ers too.
3. When Christ be - came a ser - vant and gave His life for all,
4. When at the name of Je - sus, when ev - 'ry knee shall bow,

Let each es - teem the oth - er a - bove them-selves and find:
Strive not in vain and glo - ry, in an - y - thing you do.
With self - less, hum - ble love, He o - beyed His Fa - ther's call.
Then ev - 'ry tongue con - fess - es the God of glo - ry now.

CHORUS

Then with God's own love, be of one mind, and live in one ac - cord;

Al - ways let this mind be in you, the mind of Christ our Lord.

TEXT: Philippians 2:1-11
MUSIC: Ross Jutsum

Blest Be the Tie

"Fulfil ye my joy, that ye be likeminded" (Philippians 2:2)

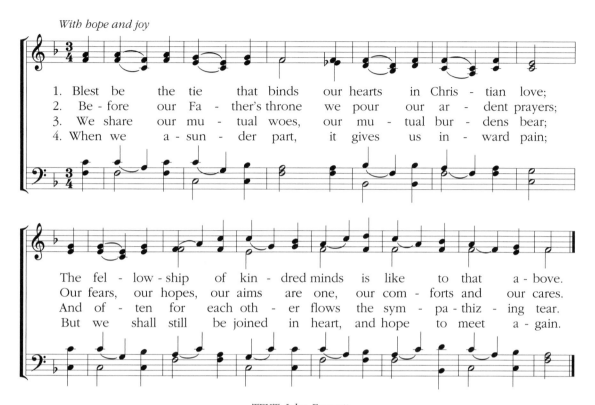

With hope and joy

1. Blest be the tie that binds our hearts in Chris - tian love;
2. Be - fore our Fa - ther's throne we pour our ar - dent prayers;
3. We share our mu - tual woes, our mu - tual bur - dens bear;
4. When we a - sun - der part, it gives us in - ward pain;

The fel - low - ship of kin - dred minds is like to that a - bove.
Our fears, our hopes, our aims are one, our com - forts and our cares.
And of - ten for each oth - er flows the sym - pa - thiz - ing tear.
But we shall still be joined in heart, and hope to meet a - gain.

TEXT: John Fawcett
MUSIC: Hans G. Naegeli

Rejoice, the Lord Is King!

"Rejoice in the Lord alway: and again I say, Rejoice" (Philippians 4:4)

Majestically

1. Re - joice, the Lord is King! Your Lord and King a - dore!
2. The Lord, our Sav - ior, reigns, the God of truth and love;
3. His King-dom can - not fail; He rules o'er earth and heav'n;

Re - joice, give thanks and sing and tri - umph ev - er - more:
When He had purged our stains, He took His seat a - bove:
The keys of death and hell are to our Je - sus giv'n:

CHORUS

Lift up your heart; lift up your voice!

Re - joice, a - gain I say, Re - joice!

TEXT: Charles Wesley, based on Philippians 4:4
MUSIC: John Darwall

O for a Thousand Tongues

"And that every tongue should confess that Jesus Christ is Lord" (Philippians 2:11)

With joyous reverence

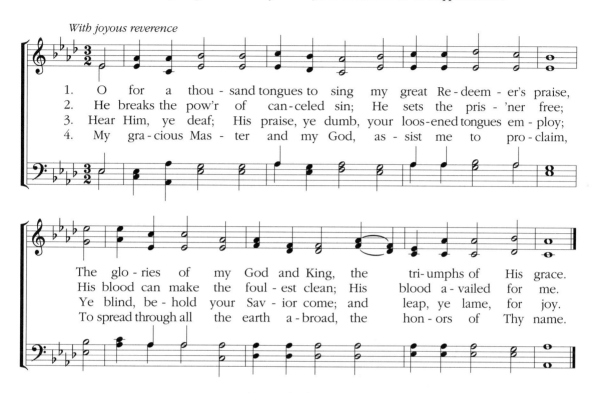

1. O for a thou - sand tongues to sing my great Re - deem - er's praise,
2. He breaks the pow'r of can - celed sin; He sets the pris - 'ner free;
3. Hear Him, ye deaf; His praise, ye dumb, your loos - ened tongues em - ploy;
4. My gra - cious Mas - ter and my God, as - sist me to pro - claim,

The glo - ries of my God and King, the tri - umphs of His grace.
His blood can make the foul - est clean; His blood a - vailed for me.
Ye blind, be - hold your Sav - ior come; and leap, ye lame, for joy.
To spread through all the earth a - broad, the hon - ors of Thy name.

TEXT: Charles Wesley
MUSIC: Carl G. Gläzer; arranged by Lowell Mason

Think on These Things

"If there be any virtue, and if there be any praise..." (Philippians 4:8)

With determination

1. What-ev-er is love-ly and true, what-ev-er is gra-cious and kind,
2. In psalms and in spir-i-tual songs, in hymns as we of-fer our praise,

What-ev-er is just and is pure, with these we should fill up our minds.
We speak to each oth-er in love, as voic-es to-geth-er we raise.

If an-y-thing wor-thy of praise and vir-tue of which we could sing;
So glad-den your-selves in the Lord; de-light and re-joice all the day.

What's wor-thy of hon-or and rev-'rence, my breth-ren, let's think on these things.
My breth-ren, let's think on these things and we'll walk in His won-der-ful way.

TEXT: Ephesians 5:19 & Philippians 4:8
MUSIC: Ross Jutsum

It Is Well With My Soul

"For I have learned, in whatsoever state I am, therewith to be content" (Philippians 4:11)

Peacefully

1. When peace, like a riv - er, at - tend - eth my way,
2. Though Sa - tan should buf - fet, though tri - als should come,
3. My sin, oh, the bliss of this glo - ri - ous thought:
4. And, Lord, haste the day when the faith shall be sight,

When sor - rows like sea bil - lows roll;
Let this blest as - sur - ance con - trol,
My sin not in part, but the whole,
The clouds be rolled back as a scroll;

What - ev - er my lot, Thou hast taught me to say,
That Christ has re - gard - ed my help - less es - tate,
Is nailed to the cross and I bear it no more;
The trump shall re - sound and the Lord shall de - scend;

"It is well, it is well with my soul."
And hath shed His own blood for my soul.
Praise the Lord, praise the Lord, O my soul!
E - ven so, it is well with my soul.

TEXT: Horatio G. Spafford
MUSIC: Philip P. Bliss

Immortal, Invisible, God Only Wise

"Now unto the King eternal, immortal, invisible, the only wise God" (I Timothy 1:17)

In jubilant style

1. Im - mor - tal, in - vis - i - ble, God on - ly wise,
2. Un - rest - ing, un - hast - ing, and si - lent as light,
3. Great Fa - ther of glo - ry, pure Fa - ther of light,

In light in - ac - ces - si - ble hid from our eyes,
Nor want - ing, nor wast - ing, Thou rul - est in might;
Thine an - gels a - dore Thee, all hail - ing Thy might;

Most bless - ed most glo - rious, the An - cient of Days,
Thy jus - tice like moun - tains high soar - ing a - bove,
All laud we would ren - der: O help us to see

Al - might - y, vic - to - rious, Thy great name we praise.
Thy clouds which are foun - tains of good - ness and love.
'Tis on - ly the splen - dor of light hid - eth Thee.

TEXT: Walter Chalmers Smith, 1867
MUSIC: Traditional Welsh Hymn melody

Fight the Good Fight

"Fight the good fight of faith" (I Timothy 6:12)

Fervently

1. Fight the good fight with all thy might!
2. Run the straight race through God's good grace;
3. Cast care a - side; lean on thy guide;
4. Faint not nor fear, His arms are near;

Christ is thy strength, and Christ thy right.
Lift up thine eyes, and seek His face.
His bound - less mer - cy will pro - vide.
He chang - eth not, and thou art dear.

Lay hold on life, and it shall be
Life with its way be - fore us lies;
Trust, and thy trust - ing soul shall prove
On - ly be - lieve, and thou shalt see

Thy joy and crown e - ter - nal - ly.
Christ is the path, and Christ the prize.
Christ is its life, and Christ its love.
That Christ is all in all to thee.

TEXT: John S. B. Monsell
MUSIC: William Boyd

266

At One With God

"...to make reconciliation for the sins of the people" (Hebrews 2:17)

CHORUS

We re-joice with our God through our Lord, Je-sus Christ;

Rec-on-ciled by the death of His Son.

We are bought with a price, and we're saved by His life;

By His grace, we're at peace and at one.

TEXT: Romans 5:8-11, 9:33, Hebrews 2:11, 9:12, 24, 10:19-21 & I John 1:9
MUSIC: Ross Jutsum

I Sing the Mighty Power of God

"And God did rest the seventh day from all His works" (Hebrews 4:4)

TEXT: Isaac Watts
MUSIC: From Gesangbuch der Herzogl, Württemberg, 1784

Safely Through Another Week

"There remaineth therefore a rest to the people of God" (Hebrews 4:9)

Gratefully

1. Safe - ly through an - oth - er week, God has brought us on our way;
2. While we seek sup - plies of grace through the great Re - deem - er's name,
3. May Thy gos - pel's joy - ful sound con - quer sin - ners, com - fort saints;

Let us now a bless - ing seek, wait - ing in His courts to - day;
Show Thy rec - on - cil - ing face; take a - way our sin and shame;
Make the fruits of grace a - bound; bring re - lief from all com - plaints;

Day of all the week the best, em - blem of e - ter - nal rest;
From our world - ly cares set free, may we rest, this day, in Thee;
Thus let all our Sab - baths prove, till on earth Thy King - dom come;

Day of all the week the best, em - blem of e - ter - nal rest.
From our world - ly cares set free, may we rest, this day, in Thee.
Thus let all our Sab - baths prove, till on earth Thy king - dom come.

TEXT: John Newton
MUSIC: Lowell Mason

Faith of Our Fathers

"The just shall live by faith" (Hebrews 10:38)

Devoutly

1. Faith of our fa - thers, liv - ing still,
2. Faith of our fa - thers, faith and prayer,
3. Faith of our fa - thers; we will love

In spite of dun - geon, fire and sword:
Keep - ing our coun - try brave and free,
Both friend and foe in all our strife:

O how our hearts beat high with joy,
And through the truth that comes from God,
And preach Thee, too, as love knows how,

When - e'er we hear the glo - rious word!
His chil - dren have true lib - er - ty.
By kind - ly words and vir - tuous life:

Faith of our fa - thers, ho - ly faith!
Faith of our fa - thers, ho - ly faith!
Faith of our fa - thers, ho - ly faith!

We will be true to Thee till death!
We will be true to Thee till death!
We will be true to Thee till death!

TEXT: Frederick W. Faber
MUSIC: Henri F. Hemy

All Hail the Power

"To whom be glory for ever and ever" (Hebrews 13:21)

With nobility and reverence

1. All hail the pow'r of Je-sus' name! Let an-gels pros-trate fall;
2. Ye cho-sen seed of Is-rael's race, ye who did hear the call,
3. Let ev-'ry kin-dred, ev-'ry tribe, on this ter-res-trial ball,
4. O that, with yon-der an-gel throng, we at His feet may fall!

Be-hold the roy-al di-a-dem, and crown Him Lord of all;
Praise Him who saves you by His grace, and crown Him Lord of all;
To Him all maj-es-ty as-cribe, and crown Him Lord of all;
We'll join the ev-er-last-ing song, and crown Him Lord of all;

Be-hold the roy-al di-a-dem, and crown Him Lord of all!
Praise Him who saves you by His grace, and crown Him Lord of all!
To Him all maj-es-ty as-cribe, and crown Him Lord of all!
We'll join the ev-er-last-ing song, and crown Him Lord of all!

TEXT: Edward Perronet & John Rippon
MUSIC: Oliver Holden

Pure Religion

"...to visit the fatherless and widows in their affliction" (James 1:27)

With sincerity

1. Pure re - li - gion un - de - filed be-fore our God and Fa - ther;
2. Ev - 'ry good and pleas-ant gift, it comes from God a - bove;

Pure re - li - gion from the heart draws us all to - geth - er.
Com - ing from the Lord of Lights, from the God of love.

Vis - it or - phans in their grief, wid - ows in dis - tress.
Of His own will brought us forth, by His Word com - mands;

Keep un - spot - ted from the world, grow in righ - teous - ness.
Leads us by His per - fect truth, first - fruits of His plan.

TEXT: James 1:17, 27
MUSIC: Ross Jutsum

The Wisdom From Above

"...is first pure, then peaceable, gentle, and easy to be entreated" (James 3:17)

Peacefully

1. In - cline your ear to wis - dom, and your heart to un - der - stand - ing:
2. The Gos - pel tells of vir - gins who went out to meet the bride - groom,
3. The man who hears God's teach - ings, who goes out and then o - beys them,
4. Yes, hap - py is the per - son who in - clines his heart to wis - dom,

It's more pre - cious than ru - bies and bet - ter far than gold.
And the wise ones their ves - sels with oil they did pro - vide.
He is just like the wise man who builds up - on a rock.
Its in - struc - tion and coun - sel will save them from the snare.

The Lord gives us His wis - dom, knowl - edge and un - der - stand - ing,
The call came in at mid - night, sum - moned them all to meet Him,
The rain de - scend - ed, winds blew, beat - ing with force and fu - ry,
Speak truth and live sin - cere - ly; shun pride, de - ceit and false ways.

He lays it up for the righ - teous who His laws and com - mand - ments hold.
The five wise vir - gins were read - y to go in and with Him a - bide.
The house will stand with - out shak - ing, for it's found - ed up - on a Rock.
The bless - ings will sure - ly fol - low and from e - vil you will be spared.

CHORUS

The wis-dom from a-bove is pure and al-ways peace-ful;

It's gen-tle, com-pli-ant and in mer-cy will in-crease.

This wis-dom from a-bove is im-par-tial and sin-cere;

It sows the fruit of righ-teous-ness, brings ev-er-last-ing peace.

TEXT: Proverbs 2:6-7, Proverbs 8:10-11, Matthew 7:24-27; 25:1-13; James 3:17
MUSIC: Ruth Myrick

Fervent Prayer

"The prayer of a righteous man is powerful and effective" (James 5:16)

With humility

1. Is an-y-one suff-'ring, let him pray; is an-y-one cheer-ful, sing God's praise.
2. Is an-y af-flic-ted, let him pray; is an-y-one hum-ble, have no shame.

Call for the el-ders of the Church and let your prayers to God be raised.
Faith-ful prayers will save the weak; a-noint with oil in God's great name.

CHORUS

Pray for each oth-er that you may be healed; let your re-quests to God be made.

All fer-vent prayer of the righ-teous man prof-its much when bold-ly prayed.

TEXT: James 5:13-16
MUSIC: Ross Jutsum

A Chosen Generation

"...a royal priesthood, an holy nation, a peculiar people" (I Peter 2:9)

Humbly

1. You're a cho-sen gen-er-a-tion, roy-al priest-hood for His throne;
2. Once you were not called a peo-ple in a world that's gone a-stray;
3. You're a cho-sen gen-er-a-tion, roy-al priest-hood for His throne;

You're a blessed and ho-ly na-tion; you're a peo-ple for His own.
Now you've heed-ed His great call-ing, show-ing forth His will and way.
You're a blessed and ho-ly na-tion; you're a peo-ple for His own.

So you may de-clare His prais-es, do what's pleas-ing in His sight,
You had not re-ceived the mer-cy of E-ter-nal God a-bove;
So you may de-clare His prais-es, do what's pleas-ing in His sight,

He has called you out of dark-ness to His glo-rious, mar-v'llous light.
Now you are the blessed re-ceiv-ers of His mer-cy and His love.
He has called you out of dark-ness to His glo-rious, mar-v'llous light.

TEXT: I Peter 2:9-10
MUSIC: Ross Jutsum

Standing on the Promises

"His divine power hath given unto us...exceeding great and precious promises" (II Peter 1:3-4)

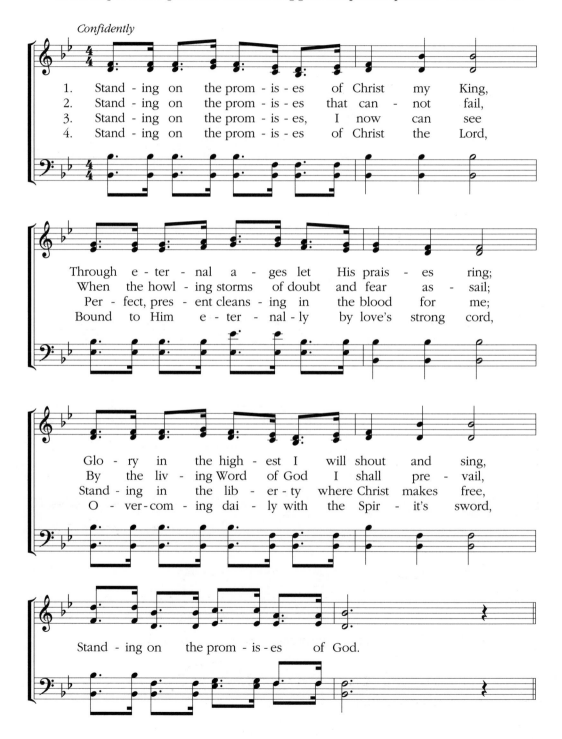

Confidently

1. Stand - ing on the prom - is - es of Christ my King,
2. Stand - ing on the prom - is - es that can - not fail,
3. Stand - ing on the prom - is - es, I now can see
4. Stand - ing on the prom - is - es of Christ the Lord,

Through e - ter - nal a - ges let His prais - es ring;
When the howl - ing storms of doubt and fear as - sail;
Per - fect, pres - ent cleans - ing in the blood for me;
Bound to Him e - ter - nal - ly by love's strong cord,

Glo - ry in the high - est I will shout and sing,
By the liv - ing Word of God I shall pre - vail,
Stand - ing in the lib - er - ty where Christ makes free,
O - ver-com - ing dai - ly with the Spir - it's sword,

Stand - ing on the prom - is - es of God.

TEXT: R. Kelso Carter
MUSIC: R. Kelso Carter

280

God Be With You

"Looking for...the coming of the day of God" (II Peter 3:12)

TEXT: J. E. Rankin
MUSIC: W. G. Tomer

Cleanse Me

"If we confess our sins, He is faithful and just...to cleanse us from all unrighteousness" (I John 1:9)

1. Search me, O God, and know my heart to-day;
2. I praise Thee, Lord, for cleans-ing me from sin;
3. Lord, take my life, and make it whol-ly Thine;

Try me, O Sav-ior, know my thoughts, I pray.
Ful-fill Thy Word and make me pure with-in.
Fill my poor heart with Thy great love di-vine.

See if there be some wick-ed way in me;
Fill me with fire, where once I burned with shame;
Take all my will, my pas-sion, self and pride;

Cleanse me from ev-'ry sin, and set me free.
Grant my de-sire to mag-ni-fy Thy name.
I now sur-ren-der, Lord; in me a-bide.

TEXT: Edwin Orr
MUSIC: Traditional Maori melody

Abide With Me

"And now...abide in Him; that, when He shall appear, we may have confidence" (I John 2:28)

Prayerfully

1. A - bide with me; fast falls the e - ven - tide;
2. I need Thy pres - ence ev - 'ry pass - ing hour;
3. I fear no foe with Thee at hand to bless;

The dark - ness deep - ens; Lord, with me a - bide;
What but Thy grace can foil the tempt - er's pow'r?
Ills have no weight and tears no bit - ter - ness;

When oth - er help - ers fail and com - forts flee,
Who like Thy - self my guide and stay can be?
Where is death's sting? Where, grave, thy vic - to - ry?

Help of the help - less, O a - bide with me.
Through cloud and sun - shine, O a - bide with me.
I tri - umph still if Thou a - bide with me.

TEXT: Henry F. Lyte
MUSIC: EVENTIDE by William H. Monk

O Brother Man

"Let us not love in word, neither in tongue; but in deed and in truth" (1 John 3:18)

With warmhearted devotion

1. O broth-er man, fold to thy heart thy broth-er;
2. For he whom Je-sus loved has tru-ly spo-ken;
3. Fol-low with rev-'rent steps the great ex-am-ple

Where pit-y dwells, the peace of God is there;
The ho-lier wor-ship which He deigns to bless
Of Him whose ho-ly work was do-ing good;

To wor-ship right-ly is to love each oth-er,
Re-stores the lost and binds the spir-it bro-ken,
So shall the wide earth seem our Fa-ther's tem-ple,

Each smile a hymn, each kind-ly deed a prayer.
And feeds the wid-ow and the fa-ther-less.
Each lov-ing life a psalm of grat-i-tude.

TEXT: John Greenleaf Whittier
MUSIC: E. Cooper Perry

Love Divine, All Love's Excelling

"God sent His only begotten Son...that we might live through Him" (I John 4:9)

With supplication

1. Love di - vine, all love's ex - cel - ling,
2. Breathe, O breathe Thy lov - ing Spir - it
3. Fin - ish then Thy new cre - a - tion;

Joy of heav'n, to earth come down;
In - to ev - 'ry trou - bled breast;
Pure and spot - less let us be;

Fix in us Thy hum - ble dwell - ing;
Let us all in Thee in - her - it;
Let us see Thy great sal - va - tion

All Thy faith - ful mer - cies crown.
Let us find Thy prom - ised rest.
Per - fect - ly re - stored in Thee.

Je - sus, Thou art all com - pas - sion;
Take a - way our bent to sin - ning;
Changed from glo - ry in - to glo - ry,

Pure, un - bound - ed love Thou art;
Al - pha and O - me - ga be;
Serve Thee as Thy hosts a - bove;

Vis - it us with Thy sal - va - tion;
End of faith, as its be - gin - ning,
Pray and praise Thee with - out ceas - ing,

En - ter ev - 'ry trem - bling heart.
Set our hearts at lib - er - ty.
Glo - ry in Thy per - fect love.

TEXT: Charles Wesley
MUSIC: Rowland H. Prichard; arranged by Robert Harkness

The Lion of Judah

"...behold, the Lion of the tribe of Judah, the Root of David, hath prevailed" (Revelation 5:5)

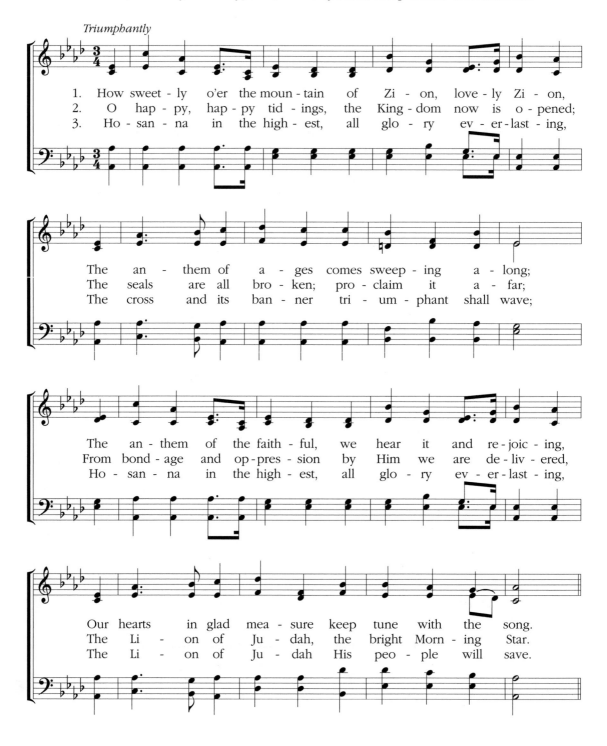

Triumphantly

1. How sweet-ly o'er the moun-tain of Zi - on, love-ly Zi - on,
2. O hap-py, hap-py tid-ings, the King-dom now is o-pened;
3. Ho-san-na in the high-est, all glo-ry ev-er-last-ing,

The an - them of a - ges comes sweep-ing a - long;
The seals are all bro-ken; pro - claim it a - far;
The cross and its ban - ner tri - um - phant shall wave;

The an - them of the faith - ful, we hear it and re - joic-ing,
From bond-age and op-pres - sion by Him we are de - liv - ered,
Ho-san - na in the high - est, all glo - ry ev - er-last - ing,

Our hearts in glad mea - sure keep tune with the song.
The Li - on of Ju - dah, the bright Morn - ing Star.
The Li - on of Ju - dah His peo - ple will save.

TEXT: Fanny J. Crosby
MUSIC: William H. Doane

To God Be the Glory

"Fear God, and give glory to Him" (Revelation 14:7)

With exultation

1. To God be the glo - ry; great things He hath done!
2. O per - fect re-demp-tion, the pur-chase of blood!
3. Great things He hath taught us; great things He hath done!

So loved He the world that He gave us His Son,
To ev - 'ry be - liev - er the prom - ise of God;
And great our re - joic - ing through Je - sus the Son;

Who yield - ed His life, an a - tone-ment for sin,
The vil - est of-fend - er who tru - ly be - lieves,
But pur - er and high - er and great - er will be

And o - pened the life - gate that all may go in.
That mo - ment from Je - sus a par - don re - ceives.
Our won - der, our trans - port, when Je - sus we see.

CHORUS

Praise the Lord; praise the Lord; let the earth hear His voice!

Praise the Lord; praise the Lord; let the peo - ple re - joice!

O come to the Fa - ther through Je - sus the Son,

And give Him the glo - ry; great things He hath done!

TEXT: Fanny J. Crosby
MUSIC: William H. Doane

For All the Saints
Who From Their Labors Rest

"Yea, saith the Spirit, that they may rest from their labours" (Revelation 14:13)

With confident devotion

1. For all the saints, who from their la - bors rest,
2. Thou wast their Rock, their For - tress, and their Might;
3. Oh, may Thy sol - diers, faith - ful, true and bold,
4. And when the strife is fierce, the war - fare long,
5. But lo, there breaks a yet more glo - rious day:

Who Thee by faith be - fore the world con - fessed,
Thou, Lord, their Cap - tain in the well - fought fight;
Fight as the saints who no - bly fought of old,
Steals on the ear the dis - tant tri - umph song,
The saints tri - um - phant rise in bright ar - ray;

Thy name, O Je - sus, be for - ev - er blest:
Thou, in the dark - ness drear, their one true Light:
And win with them the vic - tors' crown of gold:
And hearts are brave a - gain, and arms are strong:
The King of glo - ry pass - es on His way:

Al - le - lu - ia! Al - le - lu - ia!

TEXT: William Walsham How, 1864
MUSIC: SINE NOMINE by Ralph Vaughan Williams, 1906

Glory to Thy Name

"Great and marvellous are Thy works...just and true are Thy ways" (Revelation 15:3)

Majestically

1. I will ex - tol Thee, my God and King a - dore;
2. Who shall not fear Thee and glo - ri - fy Thy name,
3. Saints in Thy splen - dor shall give Thee thanks and praise;
4. Thy name I bless, Lord, my King, for - ev - er - more.

And bless Thy name, O Lord, from now and ev - er - more.
And wor - ship Thee, O Lord, through this and ev - 'ry age?
De - clare Thy great - ness, Thy won - drous works pro - claim.
King of all a - ges, all na - tions, Thee a - dore.

How just and true Thy ways, Lord, O King of ev - 'ry age.
Thy might - y deeds and judg - ments in righ - teous - ness re - vealed;
Thy King - dom and Thy pow - er in love reign-eth o - ver men.
For Thou a - lone art ho - ly, Thy good - ness pours forth fame;

How just and true Thy ways, for - ev - er glo - ry to Thy name.
Thy mer - cy lasts for - ev - er - more, we glo - ri - fy Thee, Lord.
Let all the na - tions, ev - 'ry an - gel, bless Thy ho - ly name.
O Lord, our God, and King for - ev - er, glo - ry to Thy name.

TEXT: Psalm 145:1-15 & Revelation 15:3-4
MUSIC: Sonia J. King

Battle Hymn of the Republic

"Alleluia: for the Lord God Omnipotent reigneth" (Revelation 19:6)

Victoriously

1. Mine eyes have seen the glo - ry of the com - ing of the Lord;
2. He has sound - ed forth the trum - pet that shall nev - er sound re - treat;
3. In the beau - ty of the au - tumn Christ was born a - cross the sea,

He is tram - pling out the vin - tage where the grapes of wrath are stored;
He is sift - ing out the hearts of men be - fore His judg - ment seat;
With a glo - ry in His bo - som that trans - fig - ures you and me;

He hath loosed the fate - ful light - ning of His ter - ri - ble swift sword;
O be swift my soul, to an - swer Him, be ju - bi - lant my feet!
As He lives to make men ho - ly, let us live to make men free!

REFRAIN

His truth is march - ing on.
Our God is march - ing on.   Glo - ry! Glo - ry! Hal - le - lu - jah!
While God is march - ing on.

Glory! Glory! Hal - le - lu - jah! Glo - ry! Glo - ry!

Hal - le - lu - jah! Our God is march - ing on.

His truth
While God

TEXT: *Julia Ward Howe*
MUSIC: *Traditional American melody*

Crown Him With Many Crowns

"His eyes were as a flame of fire, and on His head were many crowns" (Revelation 19:12)

Majestically; with anticipation

1. Crown Him with man - y crowns, the Lamb up - on His throne:
2. Crown Him the Lord of life: Who tri - umphed o'er the grave,
3. Crown Him the Lord of heav'n: one with the Fa - ther known,

Hark! How the heav'n-ly an - them drowns all mu - sic but its own!
Who rose vic - to - rious to the strife for those He came to save.
One with the Spir - it through Him giv'n from yon - der glo - rious throne.

A - wake, my soul, and sing of Him Who died for thee,
His glo - ries now we sing, Who died and rose on high,
To Thee be end - less praise, for Thou for us hast died;

And hail Him as thy match-less King through all e - ter - ni - ty.
Who died, e - ter - nal life to bring, and lives that death may die.
Be Thou, O Lord, through end - less days a - dored and mag - ni - fied.

TEXT: Matthew Bridges & Godfrey Thring
MUSIC: George J. Elvey

The New Jerusalem

"And I John saw the holy city, new Jerusalem, coming down from God out of heaven" (Revelation 21:2)

With eager anticipation

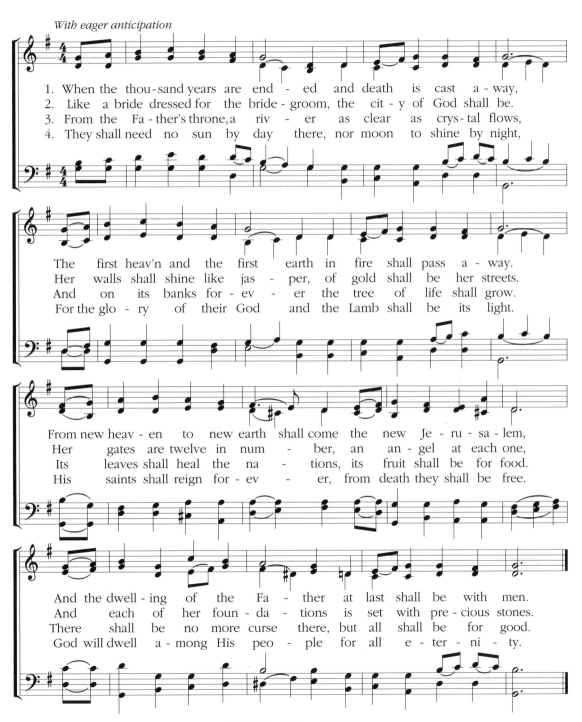

1. When the thou-sand years are end - ed and death is cast a - way,
2. Like a bride dressed for the bride - groom, the cit - y of God shall be.
3. From the Fa - ther's throne, a riv - er as clear as crys - tal flows,
4. They shall need no sun by day there, nor moon to shine by night,

The first heav'n and the first earth in fire shall pass a - way.
Her walls shall shine like jas - per, of gold shall be her streets.
And on its banks for - ev - er the tree of life shall grow.
For the glo - ry of their God and the Lamb shall be its light.

From new heav - en to new earth shall come the new Je - ru - sa - lem,
Her gates are twelve in num - ber, an an - gel at each one,
Its leaves shall heal the na - tions, its fruit shall be for food.
His saints shall reign for - ev - er, from death they shall be free.

And the dwell - ing of the Fa - ther at last shall be with men.
And each of her foun - da - tions is set with pre - cious stones.
There shall be no more curse there, but all shall be for good.
God will dwell a - mong His peo - ple for all e - ter - ni - ty.

TEXT: Revelation 21 & 22
MUSIC: Mark Graham

God Shall Wipe Every Tear

"There will be no more death or mourning or crying or pain" (Revelation 21:4)

With joyful anticipation

1. God shall wipe ev-'ry tear from their eyes, wipe ev-'ry tear a - way.
2. God shall o - pen the eyes of the blind, all of the deaf shall hear.
3. Then the ran-somed of God shall re - turn, com-ing to Zi - on sing - ing.

They shall learn then to fear their God, for - mer things shall all pass a - way.
And the tongue of the dumb shall sing, lame men will leap just like the deer.
Joy and glad - ness shall they all ob - tain, voic - es of youth will be ring - ing.

There will be no more sor - row or cry - ing, there will be no more pain or dy - ing.
Streams in the des - ert, wa - ters flow - ing, wil - der-ness pla - ces bloom-ing and grow-ing.
God will re-deem man-kind from death and give them back their life and breath.

God shall wipe ev-'ry tear from their eyes, wipe ev-'ry tear a - way.
God shall o - pen the eyes of the blind, all of the deaf shall hear.
Then all the ran-somed of God shall re - turn com - ing to Zion with song!

TEXT: Isaiah 35:1-7, 10 & Revelation 21:4
MUSIC: Ross Jutsum

For the Healing of the Nations

"...and the leaves of the tree were for the healing of the nations" (Revelation 22:2)

With earnest hope

1. For the heal-ing of the na-tions, Lord, we pray with one ac-cord;
2. Lead us, Fa-ther, in-to free-dom, from de-spair Your world re-lease;
3. All that kills a-bun-dant liv-ing, let it from the earth be banned;
4. You, Cre-a-tor God, have writ-ten Your great name on all man-kind;

For a just and e-qual shar-ing of the things that earth af-fords.
That, re-deemed from war and ha-tred, men may come and go in peace.
Pride of sta-tus, race or school-ing, dog-mas keep-ing man from man.
For our grow-ing in Your like-ness, bring the life of Christ to mind;

To a life of love in ac-tion, help us rise and pledge our word.
Show us how through care and good-ness fear will die and hope in-crease.
In our com-mon quest for jus-tice, may we hal-low life's brief span.
That by our re-sponse and ser-vice earth its des-ti-ny may find.

TEXT: Fred Kaan; Copyright,1968, by Hope Publishing Company
MUSIC: Caspar Ett's "Cantica Sacra," 1840

298

It Won't Be Long Now

"'Yes, I am coming soon'...Come, Lord Jesus" (Revelation 22:20)

With fervent anticipation

1. It won't be long now till the world is at peace,
2. It won't be long now till all peo - ple join hands

Till trou-bles have ceased, it won't be long.
From man - y a land, it won't be long.

It won't be long now till the beau-ty we see
It won't be long now till the chil-dren will smile

For the whole world will be, it won't be long.
And laugh all the while, it won't be long.

CHORUS

The lamb will peace-ful-ly dwell with the li-on,

The leop-ard will lie down with the kid.

The wolf and the bear will no long-er be wild,

Lit-tle child, it won't be long now.

TEXT: Isaiah 11:6-9 & Revelation 22:20
MUSIC: Ross Jutsum

I'll Never Leave You

"The grace of our Lord Jesus Christ be with you all. Amen." (Revelation 22:21)

With peaceful assurance

1. Five spar-rows are sold for two far - things, yet not one will fall to the ground;
2. We're giv - en a spe-cial com-mis - sion to fin - ish with all of our might;

That is, lest your heav - en - ly Fa - ther shall know for He hears ev -'ry sound.
Be - hold, lift your eyes to the har - vest, you'll see how the fields are all white.

You know you are worth more than spar - rows, He num-bers the hairs on your head.
We're bring-ing a mes-sage of good news, we'll sing to the world with one voice.

He knows all our needs and de - sires, so re - mem - ber the words He has said:
So has - ten the day when our Lord will say, "To - geth - er, let's tru - ly re - joice."

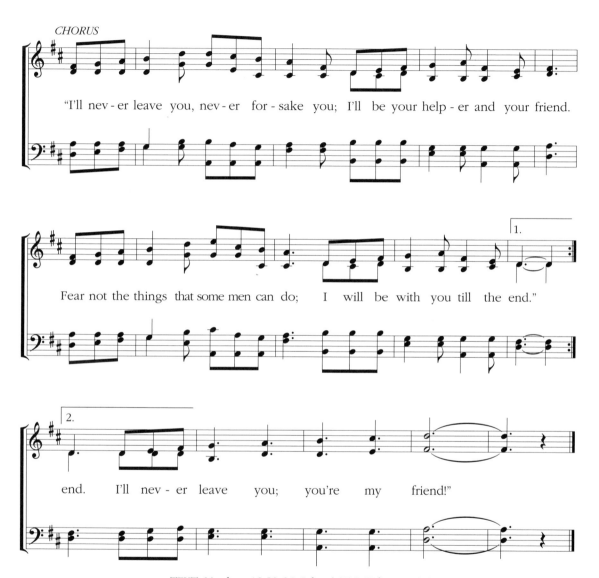

CHORUS

"I'll nev - er leave you, nev - er for - sake you; I'll be your help - er and your friend.

Fear not the things that some men can do; I will be with you till the end."

end. I'll nev - er leave you; you're my friend!"

TEXT: *Matthew 10:29-31, John 4:35 & Hebrews 13:5*
MUSIC: *Ross Jutsum*

Christic, Our Lord, Savior and King:

Christian Living:

Creation:

Faithfulness, Guidance and Protection:

Praise, Worship and Adoration:

Prayer and Supplication:

The Church of God:

All Creatures of Our God and King

Words © Copyright 1927 (Renewed) J. Curwen & Sons Ltd. All rights for the U.S. and Canada controlled by G. Schirmer, Inc. (ASCAP) (Text by St. Francis of Assisi, English translation by William Draper.) Used by permission of G. Schirmer, Inc. Music: LASST UNS ERFREUEN, arranged by Ralph Vaughan Williams (1872-1958), from the English Hymnal by permission of Oxford University Press.

Be Thou My Vision

Music: SLANE, harmonized by David Evans (1874-1948), from the Revised Church Hymnary, 1927, by permission of Oxford University Press.

Eternal Father, Strong to Save

From *The Hymnal,* 1982, © Copyright, The Church Pension Fund.

For All the Saints Who From Their Labors Rest

Lyrics by William W. How. Music by Ralph Vaughan Williams. Used by permission of J. Curwen & Sons Ltd.

For the Healing of the Nations

Words © Copyright 1968 by Hope Publishing Company, Carol Stream, IL 60188. All rights reserved. Used by permission.

God of Grace and God of Glory

Words used by permission of Elinor Fosdick Downs. Music © Copyright by E.P. Hughes. Reproduced by permission.

Great Is Thy Faithfulness

Words by Thomas O. Chisholm. Music by William M. Runyan. © Copyright 1923. Renewal 1951 by Hope Publishing Co., Carol Stream, IL 60188. All rights reserved. Used by permission.

How Great Thou Art

Lyrics and Music by Stuart K. Hine. © Copyright 1953 (Renewed 1981) by Manna Music, Inc., 25510 Stanford Ave., Valencia, CA 91355. International Copyright Secured. All rights reserved. Used by permission.

Let All Things Now Living

Lyrics by Katherine K. Davis. Music: ASHGROVE, Traditional Welsh Melody.
Used by permission of E.C. Schirmer.

Morning Has Broken

Text by Eleanor Fargeon, from the book *The Children's Bells,* published by Oxford University Press.

One Faith, One Love

Music: © Copyright, Breitkopf & Hartel, Wiesbaden.
Text: © Copyright, Paula Marler Johnson.

We Are God's People

Words: Bryan Jeffery Leech. Music: Johannes Brahms, arr. by Fred Bock. © Copyright 1976 by Fred Bock Music Company. All rights reserved. Used by permission.

All hymns by Dwight Armstrong are copyrighted by the Worldwide Church of God.
Hymns on pages 36-37, 47, 48, 49, 111, 115, 139 © copyright Worldwide Church of God, 1952, 1993.
Hymns on pages 61, 66, 67, 70, 97, 137, 157, © copyright Worldwide Church of God, 1958, 1993
Remaining hymns by Dwight Armstrong, © copyright Worldwide Church of God, 1974, 1993.

Music and/or text by David Bilowus, Sarah Bilowus, Mark Graham, Thomas Hammett, Ross Jutsum, Sonia J. King, Paul Kurts, Ruth Myrick and Caroline Sag are copyrighted by their respective composers and/or lyricists and used by permission.

All scriptural quotations used under hymn titles are from the King James Version of the Holy Bible except those on pages 57, 64, 69, 172, 173, 176, 193, 195, 212, 216, 221, 236, 243, 246, 250, 276, 296 and 298, which are from The Holy Bible, New International Version. © Copyright 1973, 1978, 1984, International Bible Society. Used by permission of Zondervan Publishing House.

Note: Every effort has been made to locate the owners of copyrighted material used in this publication. Upon notification, the publisher will make proper correction and/or addition in subsequent printings. Any omission or inaccuracy of copyright notices on individual hymns will be corrected in subsequent printings wherever valid information is offered by the claimants.

For additional information contact:
Ambassador College,
Music Department,
P.O. Box 111, Big Sandy, TX 75755.